NITROGEN FIXATION
IN PLANTS

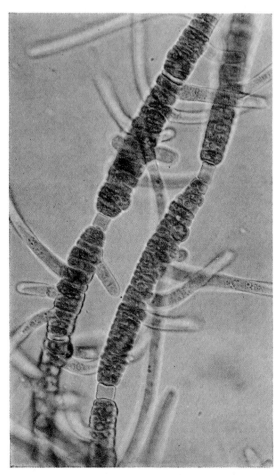

Fischerella, a nitrogen-fixing blue-green alga

Nitrogen Fixation in Plants

by

WILLIAM D. P. STEWART

B. Sc., Ph. D.

Lecturer in Botany at Westfield College,
University of London

UNIVERSITY OF LONDON
THE ATHLONE PRESS
1966

Published by
THE ATHLONE PRESS
UNIVERSITY OF LONDON
at 2 *Gower Street, London* W C I
Distributed by Constable & Co Ltd
12 *Orange Street, London* W C2

Canada
Oxford University Press
Toronto

U.S.A.
Oxford University Press Inc
New York

Printed in Great Britain by
WESTERN PRINTING SERVICES LTD
BRISTOL

To the memory of my
MOTHER *and* FATHER

Preface

Nitrogen is the cornerstone of the proteins—the building blocks for the synthesis of cell protoplasm. Despite this, few general accounts are available of biological nitrogen fixation—the process which provides a high proportion of the combined nitrogen now in circulation on the surface of the Earth. This book is an attempt to provide a brief outline of the field of nitrogen fixation. It has been built up round a series of lectures which I give at Westfield College to undergraduate botany students who have read some chemistry. It is not a complete monograph on the subject but numerous references have been included in the hope that it will prove useful not only to undergraduates but also to postgraduates and other workers.

The fact that this book has ever been written owes a great deal to my former teacher and mentor, Professor G. Bond, University of Glasgow, and to my present chief, Professor G. E. Fogg, F.R.S. I am grateful for their continuous help and encouragement, and for their friendship and wise counsel. Both have read through the entire manuscript, as has my colleague Dr. Peter Fay. Professor L. Fowden, F.R.S. has kindly read through Chapter 8—Biochemistry of Nitrogen Fixation. I am very grateful to them all for their constructive criticism; any imperfections which remain are mine, not theirs.

I should also like to thank the various authors referred to elsewhere, who have allowed me to reproduce their tables, plates and unpublished data, and the Athlone Press for their courtesy and co-operation. Finally I owe a special debt of gratitude to my wife for her help in so many ways.

March, 1965   W.D.P.S.

ACKNOWLEDGEMENTS

The author gratefully thanks the following authors, editors and firms for permission to reproduce illustrations and for kindly lending blocks or original photographs for this purpose:

Frontispiece: Dr G. H. Schwabe and Carl Zeiss Ltd, Jena (from *Zeiss Information No. 50*, page 132).

Plate 1a: Professor G. Bond (unpublished).

Plate 1b: Professor G. Bond and the editors of *Annals of Botany*, London (from *Ann. Bot.* N.S. **18**, 385).

Plates 2a, 2b: Dr P. J. Dart and the editors of *Archiv für Mikrobiologie* (from ref. 133).

Plate 4a: Professor G. Bond and the editors of *Symp. Soc. Gen. Microbiol.*, No. 13 (from ref. 80).

Plate 4b: Dr J. H. Becking and the editors of *Antonie van Leeuwenhoek* (from ref. 44).

Plate 5a: Dr J. H. Becking (unpublished).

Plate 5b: Dr Isobel C. Gardner and the editors of *Archiv für Mikrobiologie* (from ref. 211).

Plates 6a, 6b: Professor G. Bond and the editors of *Plant and Soil* (from ref. 498).

Plate 7a: Dr W. Menke and the editors of *Zeitschrift für Naturforschung* (from ref. 338).

Plate 7b: Dr J. H. Becking and the editors of *Plant and Soil* (from ref. 42).

Contents

1 Introduction

Chemical analyses show that the four most abundant elements present in plant tissues are usually carbon, hydrogen, oxygen and nitrogen. Of these, the first three are available to the plant in ample supply from atmospheric and soil sources, primarily as carbon dioxide, water and oxygen. Nitrogen on the other hand is in a somewhat different category in that while an abundant supply is present in the elemental form in the atmosphere (approximately 80 per cent by volume of the air is molecular nitrogen) the vast majority of plants cannot use it, being dependent on the relatively small quantities of combined nitrogen present in the soil, largely in the form of nitrates and ammonium-nitrogen.

It is now well established, however, that a small minority of plants can utilize gaseous nitrogen as sole nitrogen source, and under optimal conditions may grow as satisfactorily on it as they would do on combined nitrogen. Plants which assimilate elemental nitrogen are said to *fix* nitrogen and this is the context in which the term *nitrogen fixation* will be used throughout this monograph.

The suggestion that plants may fix nitrogen was made by Humphry Davy who, in the 1836 edition of his textbook *Elements of Agricultural Chemistry*,[140] wrote: 'when glutinous and albuminous substances exist in plants the azote they contain may be suspected to be derived from the atmosphere'. Evidence supporting this hypothesis was obtained by Boussingault in 1838[86] and Atwater in 1885[26] for legumes, and by Jodin in 1862[285] and Berthelot in 1885[60] for micro-organisms, but they were unable to explain their findings fully. The German workers Hellriegel and Wilfarth were therefore the first to do so, when in 1886-8[247-9] they reported their findings as showing that legumes which bore on their roots nodules inhabited by a bacterium assimilated elemental nitrogen, whereas those without nodules did not. This was followed by the discovery in 1892 by Nobbe, Schmid, Hiltner and Hotter[389] that nodulated plants of the non-leguminous angiosperm *Elaeagnus* showed much better growth in nitrogen-deficient medium than did corresponding non-nodulated plants. Like several subsequent workers they made no attempt to measure actual gains in combined nitrogen, although it was fairly evident from many of the experimental results that nitrogen fixation must have occurred. As a result Aldrich-Blake, who in 1932[5] measured gains in total nitrogen by nodulated plants of *Casuarina equisetifolia* growing in nitrogen-free medium, was probably the first to provide definite proof of nitrogen fixation by a non-legume. In 1893 Winogradsky[597] showed that *Clostridium pastorianum* (now *C. pasteurianum*) fixed nitrogen. This was the first demonstration of nitrogen fixation by a free-living bacterium, while Drewes in 1928[156] provided the first concrete evidence of nitrogen fixation by blue-green algae (*Anabaena variabilis* and *Nostoc punctiforme*) growing in the absence of bacteria. Since these studies, the spectrum of nitrogen-fixing genera and species has been extended considerably, and the ability to fix nitrogen is now known to be a common phenomenon in groups in which it was once considered rare, for example in the blue-green algae. However, no new class of nitrogen-fixing organisms has since been discovered, with the possible exception of certain yeasts.[92,342] Claims for fixation by other organisms have not been without their advocates, for example cereals and other non-nodulated angiosperms have been suggested as fixing nitrogen.[460] Indeed it has been reported by Russian workers that non-nodulated plants such as tobacco and begonias contain nitrogen-fixing enzyme systems, but that fixation is inhibited within the plants, and can be demonstrated only in cell-free extracts.[525] This suggestion is so contrary to current views on nitrogen fixation that independent confirmation of such results is urgently required. There have also been claims, which could not be confirmed independently, of fixation in sterilized soil.[147-8]

The organisms which are now generally accepted as fixing nitrogen can be conveniently classified into two main groups as follows:

1. *Symbiotic forms*

With one possible exception (*Podocarpus*), these are dicotyledonous angiosperms which bear on their roots nodules inhabited by a microbial endophyte which has induced the formation of the nodules. Only nodulated plants have been shown to fix nitrogen and there is no evidence that either of the symbionts can do so alone. There are two main groups:

1. Nodulated members of the family Leguminosae, for example, peas (*Pisum* spp.), clovers (*Trifolium* spp.), and soya bean (*Glycine max*), in which the endophyte is a bacterium of the genus *Rhizobium*.

2. Certain non-leguminous root nodule-bearing angiosperms, for example, alder (*Alnus* spp.), bog myrtle (*Myrica gale*), and sea-buckthorn (*Hippophaë rhamnoides*), in which the endophyte is now generally considered to be an actinomycete. In the following pages the term *non-legume* will be restricted to this particular group of plants. Evidence has recently been presented that the gymnosperm *Podocarpus*, in which the endophyte comprises non-septate filaments of uncertain nature, also fixes nitrogen but the reported fixation rates are low.[57]

2. *Free-living forms*

These are micro-organisms which can assimilate elemental nitrogen without entering into symbiosis with any other organism. There are the following groups:

1. Certain bacteria, for example, *Aerobacter*, *Azotobacter*, *Beijerinckia*, *Chromatium* and *Clostridium*.

2. Certain blue-green algae, for example, *Anabaena*, *Calothrix*, *Fischerella* and *Nostoc*. Some of these may form nitrogen-fixing associations with fungi to form lichens, for example *Peltigera*; with bryophytes, for example *Blasia*; with pteridophytes, for example *Azolla*; with gymnosperms, for example *Encephalartos*; and with angiosperms, for example *Gunnera*, but unlike the legumes fixation is not dependent on the partnership.

3. Possibly certain yeasts, for example *Rhodotorula* and *Pullularia*, and actinomycetes, for example *Nocardia*.

An association which may be considered intermediate between the symbiotic and free-living nitrogen-fixing systems is that of the bacterial leaf nodules found in such plants as

Psychotria and *Pavetta*. Reliable evidence for *Psychotria* has shown that the bacterium fixes nitrogen in pure culture and in association with the plants, but that the latter are abnormal in the absence of the bacterium, even when combined nitrogen is supplied.[471]

Although it is now well established that symbiotic nitrogen-fixing associations exist, little is known of their origin, but it is probable that they developed relatively recently in the evolution of the plant kingdom. There is some palaeobotanical evidence that legumes were present in the Upper Cretaceous[103] and that the sub-family Caesalpinioideae is the most primitive, while plants akin to present-day nodulated genera have been found in the Tertiary,[353] but it is not known whether these bore nodules. It has also been thought in view of the fact that certain present-day cycads harbour nitrogen-fixing blue-green algae in their roots, that the cycads, so prevalent in the Jurassic and Cretaceous periods, may have been nitrogen-fixing.[77]

The present-day legumes, which comprise approximately seven hundred genera and fourteen thousand species, are considered to be tropical in origin, and the sub-family Caesalpinioideae is almost entirely restricted to tropical areas. Tutin considers present-day legumes as 'the ultimate twigs of an evolutionary tree whose branches can be guessed at, and whose trunk can sometimes be dimly discerned in the gloom of the tropical forests'.[526] Although most abundant in the tropics, they are world-wide in distribution. Now, because of their acknowledged importance in agriculture, some of the commoner species, particularly those of the sub-family Papilionatae, have rather similar distribution patterns to man.

The non-legumes shown to date to fix nitrogen, belong to ten genera of woody perennials classified into the orders Fagales, Myricales, Casuarinales, Rhamnales and Coriariales.[80] There is thus some evidence of phylogenetic relationships within the group. The genera comprise over two hundred species, but relatively few have been examined for the presence of nodules, let alone for nitrogen fixation. Like the legumes they are of world-wide distribution, pollen analysis data indicating that at least three: *Hippophaë*, *Alnus*,[295,506,556] and *Coriaria*,[226] were of much more widespread occurrence in the past than they are at present, and there is no reason to assume that they would not then have been able to fix nitrogen.

The origin of the free-living nitrogen-fixing organisms is equally problematical. Comparative morphology suggests that because of their low level of cell differentiation they are particularly primitive; from a physiological viewpoint recent evidence obtained using cell-free extracts has shown the fixation process to be one of reduction and that an aerobic step is unnecessary even in the aerobic bacterium *Azotobacter*.[95] Thus the ability to fix gaseous nitrogen may have become firmly established under the reducing conditions of the early Earth's atmosphere. It has also been suggested that these nitrogen-fixing micro-organisms may have evolved most rapidly during the changeover of the Earth's atmosphere from reducing to oxidizing conditions when the available supplies of combined nitrogen were likely to be depleted through the process of denitrification.[190] Fortunately, palaeobotany has provided convincing evidence for the occurrence of possible nitrogen-fixing blue-green algae during the early epochs of the Earth's history for, in the Upper Devonian, almost perfectly preserved specimens have been found.[132] So closely allied are two of these organisms to the present-day nitrogen-fixing genera *Mastigocladus*,[186] *Fischerella*,[406] and *Westelliopsis*,[415] that they have been placed in the same order—the Stigonematales. Thus, evidence for the ancient origin of nitrogen-fixing micro-organisms has been accumulated from the fields of palaeobotany, morphology, and biochemistry.

Irrespective of when nitrogen-fixing organisms originated it is evident that they have been, and are, responsible for a high proportion of the combined nitrogen now in circulation on the Earth. Any estimate of the present-day contribution of fixed nitrogen to the overall combined nitrogen status of our planet can only be approximate, but a figure of 100 million tons per annum, mainly from symbiotic sources, has been suggested.[154] This contribution of biologically fixed nitrogen to soil fertility probably far outweighs that available from all other sources of combined nitrogen (lightning, artificial fertilizers, etc.) put together. [13,324]

The ability of such organisms to contribute so much combined nitrogen so readily to soil fertility has undoubtedly been, and still is, the main stimulus behind the study of biological nitrogen fixation. In the early post-Hellriegel and Wilfarth period particular attention was paid to the morphology and anatomy of the nodules, to the endophyte, and to its mechanism of infection. Studies were also concentrated on the 'whole-plant physiology' of the various nitrogen-fixing groups and on their importance in relation to soil fertility. For reviews of this earlier work the reader should consult the monographs of Fred, Baldwin and McCoy,[201] Virtanen,[540] and Wilson.[580]

By the late 1930's it had become obvious that further major advances depended largely on the development of new techniques. The introduction of the isotopic ^{15}N method (for details see p. 8) in 1941[105] opened up a new era in the study of nitrogen fixation. It became possible to supply plants with this heavy isotope of nitrogen and to measure critically its uptake and distribution. A careful reassessment of the ability of different organisms to fix nitrogen could thus be made, studies on their physiology more rapidly expanded, and a real insight gained for the first time into the mechanism of fixation. There are numerous reviews which cover this period and also provide a guide to the earlier literature. [7,49,80,104,332,379,401,543,581,584-6]

Just as the introduction of the ^{15}N technique resulted in rapid advances in our understanding of the fixation process in the 1940's and 1950's, the discovery in 1960 of reliable methods of preparing nitrogen-fixing cell-free extracts of free-living nitrogen-fixing organisms[24-5,117-18,381,462] has had a similar effect on current investigations. It has made possible another major step in the study of the fixation process, that is, a direct study of the nitrogen-fixing enzyme systems. This method obviates one of the major difficulties of the past, that is, of ensuring that the reactions observed, and the results obtained, were connected directly with fixation and not simply with overall growth of the organism. It can be anticipated that in the years to come the contribution of studies on cell-free extracts towards an understanding of the overall mechanism of fixation will become increasingly important. Indeed, so rapid are the advances being made in this field at the moment that some of the data presented in this book will almost certainly be superseded before its printing is completed. There are several recent reviews which deal with nitrogen fixation in cell-free extracts.[119,356-7,362,380]

Methods of detecting nitrogen fixation

The question of whether an organism utilizes elemental nitrogen has sometimes been a matter of controversy. Early investigators attributed nitrogen fixation to plants which showed vigorous growth in apparently nitrogen-free medium. It is only too evident from a review of the early literature[555] that this method has proved highly unsatisfactory, particularly in the case of micro-organisms, for even although nitrogen fixation by *Azoto-bacter*[46] was first suggested on the basis of such studies it should not be forgotten that on a similar basis claims for fixation by various organisms now known not to fix nitrogen were also put forward, for example free-living *Rhizobium* species.[45] Basically, an organism can be said to fix nitrogen only when an appreciable assimilation of elemental nitrogen has been demonstrated. There are several satisfactory methods which can be used to detect this.

1. *Kjeldahl analysis*

Nitrogen fixation may be measured by inoculating the test organism into medium (preferably nitrogen-free), and determining the total combined nitrogen present in the plant plus medium at the start and at the end of the experiment. A statistically significant gain in nitrogen over an uninoculated control series run at the same time can be accepted as evidence that nitrogen fixation has occurred. Although this method for measuring total nitrogen was first introduced by Kjeldahl in 1883[296] it has been variously modified since then. Basically it involves converting the total plant nitrogen to ammonia by acid digestion, the ammonia then being distilled over into dilute acid and determined titrimetrically or colorimetrically. With a little experience the method is completely reliable if its limitations, for example it is not particularly sensitive, are appreciated. Wilson[582] considers gains of at least 5–10 μg. nitrogen per ml. of medium necessary for proof of fixation in media of low nitrogen content and considerably higher gains necessary in media of high organic content. For details of the method and its limitations the reader should consult the available reviews on the subject.[110,125,260,333,584]

2. *The use of the isotope* ^{15}N

This method[110] involves exposing the test sample to elemental nitrogen enriched with the stable isotope ^{15}N (nitrogen-fixing plants show no discrimination between the isotopes of nitrogen) for a suitable period, after which the plant nitrogen is converted to ammonia, generally by Kjeldahl digestion and distillation as described above. Elemental nitrogen released from the ammonia by the addition of sodium hypobromite as follows:

$$2NH_4^+ + 2OH^- + 3NaOBr \rightarrow N_2 + 3NaBr + 5H_2O$$

is then introduced into a mass spectrometer where the abundance of mass 28 (that is $^{14}N\,^{14}N$) and mass 29 (that is $^{14}N\,^{15}N$) in the sample is measured. From the following formula:[446]

$$\frac{100}{2R + 1} \quad \text{where } R = \frac{\text{abundance of mass 28}}{\text{abundance of mass 29}}$$

the ^{15}N content of the plant nitrogen is then determined. Ordinary nitrogen, for example in unlabelled ammonium sulphate or in plant material exposed to air, contains $0 \cdot 365 - 0 \cdot 370$ atom per cent ^{15}N, and fixation can be attributed to organisms whose nitrogen, after exposure to gaseous ^{15}N-labelled molecular nitrogen, shows an enrichment of at least $0 \cdot 015$ atom per cent ^{15}N greater than that in similar unexposed material.[110]

The advantages of the ^{15}N technique are at least twofold. First, it is at least thirty and probably one hundred times more sensitive than the conventional Kjeldahl method. Secondly, the nitrogen content of the material at the start and at the end of the experiment does not need to be known, as is essential with the Kjeldahl method, providing there is sufficient nitrogen present for mass spectrometer assay. Quantities of approximately $1 \cdot 0$ mg nitrogen are most suitable for this purpose. It is however an expensive method, even although it is possible in most instances to conserve the isotope by using partial pressures of nitrogen as low as $0 \cdot 10$ atm. and yet achieve almost optimum fixation rates.[110]

3. The use of the isotope ^{13}N

Despite the sensitivity of the ^{15}N method it is sometimes not entirely satisfactory in short-term studies where high sensitivity over a short period is desirable, for example in experiments involving cell-free extracts. To overcome this difficulty Nicholas, Silvester and Fowler successfully introduced in 1961 the use of the short-lived radioactive isotope ^{13}N as a means of measuring fixation.[384] The method involves exposing the test material to elemental ^{13}N and determining fixation by measurement of increase in its radioactivity. Although approximately 100 times more sensitive than the ^{15}N method its short half-life (10·05 minutes) makes ^{13}N suitable only for experiments which can be completed within about two hours. Also, because expensive equipment is required to generate the isotope (it requires continuous production in a cyclotron), the method is not in widespread use. High count rates are frequently obtained with controls exposed to ^{13}N unless the isotope is thoroughly flushed from the system, for example with oxygen, at the end of the exposure period. Although this method has been used to demonstrate nitrogen fixation in organisms such as *Azotobacter vinclandii* it has not, as far as the present author is aware, been used to demonstrate fixation in an organism not previously shown to fix nitrogen by the conventional methods described above. This similarly applies to the following methods:

4. The microdiffusion technique

This method[355] depends on the fact that in cell-free enzyme preparations the nitrogen fixed accumulates largely as ammonia, cell-free extracts having only a limited capacity for converting ammonia to amino-nitrogen. The quantity of ammonia present thus gives a measure of fixation.

The ammonia may be measured quantitatively and accurately by a microdiffusion method[128] which involves having a two-chambered system, one of which contains the ammonia sample, the other a known volume of acid plus indicator. Alkali (a saturated solution of potassium carbonate) is then added to the former and the system immediately sealed. After continuous shaking for one hour at room temperature all the ammonia is evolved and absorbed by the acid. It is then determined titrimetrically. This method is approximately twenty times less sensitive than the ^{15}N method, fixation of 3–5 μg. nitrogen being detected.

A useful modification, which I believe originated in Dr. R. H. Burris's labratorys is illustrated in Fig. 1. This is simply a small bottle with a screw-on cap suspended from which is an etched glass rod. The sample to be analysed for ammonia is placed in the container and the rod dipped in acid (2N HCl is suitable). Alkali is then added to the test material and the system immediately sealed. The ammonia evolved is absorbed on to the acid drop, which is then dipped in Nessler's reagent[110] and the ammonia determined colorimetrically.

5. *Manometry*

This method, which involves measuring the disappearance of nitrogen gas from a sealed system which contains the test organism, was probably first used in 1862 by Jodin, who measured the disappearance of molecular nitrogen from a sealed system containing micro-organisms.[285] Because of the difficulty in obtaining reliable controls this method is not in widespread use. Recently however, it has been used to demonstrate fixation by bacterial cell-free extracts[358] and by extracts and whole cells of blue-green algae.[130]

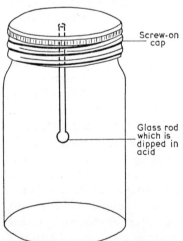

Screw-on cap

Glass rod which is dipped in acid

Fig. 1. Apparatus for measuring ammonia production using a micro-diffusion technique. (× I approx.)

2 Symbiotic Nitrogen Fixation
I. Legumes

2.1

The legumes, or strictly speaking, members of the family Leguminosae, because of their importance in soil fertility, have probably received more attention to date than has any other nitrogen-fixing group. Their beneficial effect on the soil and the importance of green manuring was realized by the ancient Chinese, Greeks and Romans[201,243,580] so that the widespread use of legumes in crop rotation was well established long before the reason why they were beneficial was discovered.

The nodules characteristic of most legumes occur laterally on the roots as small, spherical, club-shaped, or branched structures. (Plate 1, opposite p. 22.) They were certainly noted by scientists in the seventeenth century, for in drawings of bean plants made by Malpighi in 1675[330] the nodules are clearly depicted although their significance was then unknown. According to Allen and Allen[7] nodules have been detected on approximately 89 per cent of the species examined, but these represent only a small minority and the degree of nodulation of the vast majority of leguminous plants is still unknown. This applies particularly to species of tropical regions. From the available data, it appears that nodules are present on approximately 91 per cent and 94 per cent of the species of the sub-families Mimosoideae and Papilionatae respectively, but only on about 34 per cent of the Caesalpinioideae. Whether this has any phylogenetic significance is uncertain but, as mentioned earlier, the Caesalpinioideae is considered to be the most ancient of the three sub-families. The bacterial genus *Rhizobium*, which is responsible for nodule initiation and development, is a common soil organism which is not consistently seed-borne, although it is often present as a contaminant on the surface of the seed.

2.2 Tests for nitrogen fixation

The first recorded experimental evidence that leguminous plants could utilize nitrogen from the air was obtained by the French scientist Boussingault[86-7] who at Bechelbronn in Alsace, observed that when legumes such as peas and clover were grown under open unsterilized conditions they assimilated more nitrogen than was supplied to them in combined form whereas cereals such as oats and wheat did not. Unfortunately he decided to repeat his experiments using what he considered to be more precise methods, which included the use of closed containers and sterilized sand. As a result there were no rhizobia available to nodulate his plants, his earlier results were therefore not confirmed, and this, together with the criticism of his studies by Justus Liebig, the eminent agricultural chemist of the day, caused him to abandon his earlier hypothesis,[88] and it was left to Hellriegel and Wilfarth[249] to settle the controversy. Their experiments, in which they grew peas, with or without combined nitrogen, in (1) sterile sand, (2) non-sterile sand, and (3) sterile sand plus soil extract, were simple but decisive. They showed that good growth occurred in every case when combined nitrogen was supplied. In the absence of added combined nitrogen the sterile cultures did not nodulate and little growth occurred; in non-sterile sand only a few plants which had become nodulated made good growth, while in the presence of unsterilized soil extract all plants formed nodules and showed growth which was often equal to that in the presence of combined nitrogen. They thus established that only plants bearing nodules fixed nitrogen, and postulated that the nodules were the nitrogen-fixing sites, that they were formed as a result of infection of the roots by soil bacteria, and that non-nodulated plants were similar to cereals in that they required combined nitrogen for growth. In 1888 Beijerinck isolated in pure culture a bacterium which caused nodules to form on legume roots and termed it *Bacillus radicicola*.[45] Later, Frank[198] gave it the name *Rhizobium leguminosarum*, a name which is still in use. Various aspects of the history of biological nitrogen fixation are covered in detail in the monographs of Fred, Baldwin and McCoy[201] and Wilson[580] and in an interesting and entertaining paper by Wilson.[583]

The validity of Hellriegel and Wilfarth's findings has been demonstrated hundreds and probably thousands of times. Tests have generally been carried out by growing the plants in the absence of combined nitrogen, gains in total nitrogen by nodulated plants over controls of non-nodulated plants being used as a measure of fixation. In symbiotic systems of this type where the fixation rate is rapid, this is a perfectly reliable and cheap method of demonstrating fixation. The more costly isotopic method has also been frequently employed, confirmatory evidence of the long-term growth analyses generally being obtained. Using the latter method it has been possible to confirm that the nodules are the actual nitrogen-fixing sites, for detached nodules when exposed to ^{15}N incorporate the isotope readily, whereas other parts of the plant show no enrichment.[22,33] The nitrogen-fixing ability of detached nodules is retained for a short time only, suggesting that material from the host plant is necessary for fixation. Although nodules are the nitrogen-fixing sites, not all nodules necessarily fix nitrogen. Those which do are generally large, and pink in colour due to an abundant haemoglobin content (see 2.3); those which do not are termed *ineffective* nodules and tend to be small, white, more numerous, and restricted to the lateral roots.

2.3 Nodule development and structure

The sequence of events in the development of the nodule is extremely complex. All the stages referred to in the following account have not been found in all species, indeed all may not be present. Although it is well known that nodules are initiated when rhizobia enter the root cortex, it is difficult to establish which is the primary step in the chain of events leading to their ultimate formation. One of the earliest is the production by the roots of material which attracts the rhizobia towards the root hairs, and which according to Thornton is not produced until the first true leaf opens.[519] Thus, young seedlings when planted alongside older ones may nodulate earlier than they would if grown alone,[326,398] because the stimulatory substance is already present. The earlier nodulation may also be because the previously grown plants remove from the rhizosphere concentrations of nitrate inhibitory to nodulation.[222] According to the electron microscope studies of Dart and Mercer[137] the bacteria become aggregated, often as many as eight deep, in a thin layer of electron-dense material which surrounds the young roots and which is limited on the outside by a membrane. The exact nature of the stimulatory material which first attracts the rhizobia is uncertain but it has been suggested that biotin may be important.[564] However, amino acids, enzymes, sugars, and vitamins have all been recorded as occurring in root exudates.[448] It has also been shown that the secretions produced by a particular legume stimulate multiplication of rhizobial strains effective for that species more than ineffective ones or other bacteria.[401]

The bacteria then secrete material which causes many of the root-hairs to curl and become crook-shaped. This may be B-indolylacetic acid (IAA) for pure IAA and filtrates from rhizobia and other bacteria also induce root-hair curling.[217, 512] It is also known that IAA may be produced by rhizobia from tryptophan[292] excreted by the roots.[447] Substances resembling the gibberellins, another class of plant growth substances, have also been reported in rhizobial filtrates.[404] Although root-hair curling is characteristic of most infections it is doubtful whether it has any direct rôle in the process of infection, for non-curled roots have been found on occasion to contain infection threads.[400] Once root-hair curling has occurred the host then produces extracellularly the enzyme polygalacturonase in response to a stimulus caused by specific infective rhizobia.[172] The exact rôle of this enzyme in nodule initiation is uncertain but it may act together with the growth substances to increase plasticity of the root-hair wall, perhaps by loosening the cellulosic cross-links.[113]

Once the rhizosphere bacteria have been stimulated and the root-hairs preconditioned, infection of the root occurs generally at, or just lateral to, a root-hair apex, where it is marked by the presence of a small refractile spot (this may be due to changes in the arrangement of the cell-wall fibrils), and the formation of a bulge. In some instances infection occurs via broken epidermal cells,[61] and in aquatic plants with no root-hairs ordinary epidermal cells become infected.[457] When root-hairs become infected the bacteria move upwards towards the cell nucleus in the form of a thread-like non-septate structure—the infection thread. There is probably some relationship between the tip of the infection thread and the root-hair nucleus as both remain in close proximity as the infection thread moves through the hair.[171,400] The infection threads, which contain the rhizobia embedded in what appears to be a mucilaginous matrix, extend from the root hairs into the cortex, possibly via pits in the cell walls and along the middle lamellae of the cortical cells, until they penetrate cells which are to become infected, and there the rhizobia are released.[133]

The exact manner and mechanism of release is not settled unequivocally and various possibilities have been put forward by different workers, depending to some extent on their interpretation of the structures involved, particularly the nature of the wall surrounding the intracellular thread. Early workers considered it to be a mucilaginous sheath produced by the penetrating bacteria. Others suggested it was a tubular structure of host rather than bacterial origin, somewhat similar to the cell walls, and which functioned as a defence barrier against bacterial infection. Nutman, in 1956,[396] pointed out however that the earlier hypotheses suggest actual penetration of the root-hair wall and yet there is no evidence of mechanical penetration, or of rhizobia producing enzymes which digest the cell wall. He therefore suggested that the wall surrounding the infection thread is not only akin to the host cell wall—it is the host cell wall which becomes invaginated at the point of bacterial infection, and which increases in size, possibly by the process of intussusception. This implies that there is no contact between the rhizobia and the root-hair protoplasm. Evidence that this wall is of host cell wall origin rather than bacterial origin has been obtained recently from electron microscope studies.[151,366] For example Mosse[366] has distinguished clearly four regions external to the bacteria: (1) a matrix probably of bacterial origin, (2) the middle lamella of the host cell, (3) the cell wall of the host cell, and (4) the plasmalemma of the host cell. Thus it seems probable that both the host cell wall and plasmalemma become invaginated. In Plate 2a (opposite p. 23.) two infection threads which are developing from a mass of rhizobia can be seen penetrating two adjacent cells.

Before the rhizobia enter a host cell they must pass out of the infection thread. This they can do because either there is no cell wall round the growing tip of the infection thread, the bacteria being surrounded simply by the matrix and the host cell plasmalemma,[366] or if a cell wall is present gaps develop in it.[151] In some species the host cell plasmalemma swells up to form a vesicle into which the bacteria become aggregated before it ruptures and the bacteria are released.[288,366,514] Having passed out of the infection thread the bacteria become surrounded by a membrane,[134] the origin of which has been variously interpreted. It has been claimed that it is formed from the plasmalemma which is 'pinched off' round the bacteria either singly,[151] or in groups,[56] that it is synthesized *de novo*,[135] or derived from the endoplasmic reticulum of the host cell.[288,366]

At this stage the bacteria are still typical gram-negative organisms capable of division but they then increase in size, and in most plants assume a diversity of shapes—generally rod, club, X, T, or Y shapes—stop dividing, and are then called bacteroids. Typical bacteroids of *Trifolium subterraneum* are seen in Plate 2*b* (opposite p. 23). Mature bacteroids may occupy a volume forty times as great as an original *Rhizobium* cell,[151] and result in a ten-fold increase in size of the infected cell.[124] Under the light microscope the bacteroids are banded and granular in appearance; under the electron microscope they are seen to contain a marked intra-cytoplasmic membrane system not found in rod-shaped rhizobia.[136] Eventually the bacteroids completely fill the host cell, apart from the central nuclear area, the vacuole, and the periphery where the contents of the host cell cytoplasm become aggregated.

It is clear that the structural features of the infection thread and infected region are still imperfectly understood. Only time and more investigation will resolve the uncertainties. In the meantime there seems little doubt that the wall surrounding the infection thread is of host plant rather than bacterial origin, and that in the mature infected cells the bacteroids are enclosed in a membrane system again of host cell origin.

The infected cells and thus the sites of nodule initiation are generally to be found in the inner cortex although pericyclic cells may sometimes be involved.[515] Wipf and Cooper[598-600] made the interesting observation that within this region nodule initiation was dependent on the genetic constitution of the cortical cells. They showed that the cortex of normal diploid plants contains, in addition to diploid cells, certain larger tetraploid cells. The latter are present in uninoculated plants so that infection is presumably not responsible for the doubling of the chromosome number. When an infection thread comes near a tetraploid cell it apparently stimulates it, and the surrounding cells, to meristematic activity. There is no such stimulus when an ordinary diploid cell is penetrated. These findings have been independently confirmed.[207] The tetraploid cells then become infected as they are produced by division to form the infected region of the nodule. Continued division of both diploid and tetraploid cells results eventually in the formation of a nodule. Similarly in tetraploid host plants, nodules are initiated when octaploid cells become infected. Recent studies on the mechanism of infection have been reviewed by Nutman[401] and by Dart and Mercer.[137] Some of the stages associated with nodule formation are shown diagrammatically in Fig. 2 (p. 18).

The mature nodule may vary markedly in shape depending on the host and rhizobial strain but many show in longitudinal section an arrangement of tissues somewhat similar to that presented in Fig. 2e. That is:

1. An outer cortical region of undifferentiated parenchyma which sometimes contains cell inclusions such as tannins. In perennial nodules the peripheral cells may be suberized and thickened.

2. A meristematic region which is frequently apical in position but which varies depending on the legume. In some, for example in soya bean, there is no distinct growing point.[48] Apical meristems when present may dichotomize to give branched nodules.

3. The vascular tissue, which is internal to the cortex, is initiated early on in nodule development and is continuous with the vascular supply of the root. Each vascular strand is surrounded by an endodermis, and in some legumes, for example *Pisum* and *Phaseolus* species, a second endodermis—the nodule endodermis—almost completely separates the entire vascular tissue and infected region from the cortex.[200]

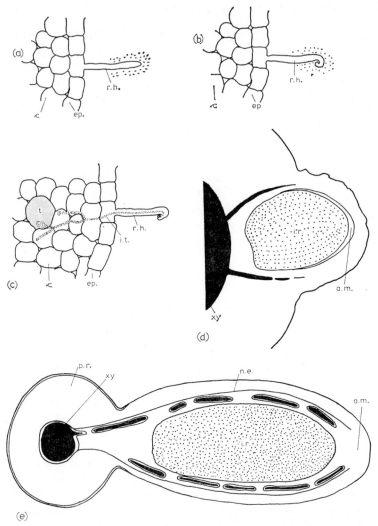

Fig. 2. Initiation and structure of pea nodules: (a) Rhizobia aggregate round root hairs. (b) Root hairs curl. (c) Rhizobia infect root hair and move through the root hair and inner cortex until they enter a tetraploid cell. This stimulates meristematic activity. (d) A central infected region and apical meristem become distinguished. (e) Longitudinal section through nodule showing central infected region, apical meristem and nodule endodermis. (a.m.: apical meristem; c.: cortex; ep.: epidermis; i.r.: infected region; i.t.: infection thread; n.e.: nodule endodermis; p.r.: primary root; r.h.: root hair; t.: tetraploid cell; xy.: xylem.)

4. The central infected area which is separated from the vascular tissue by several rows of parenchyma. In this region, associated with the swollen infected cells, is the red pigment haemoglobin, a pigment almost identical with the haemoglobins which act as oxygen carriers in mammalian respiratory systems. Although sometimes designated leg-haemoglobin it is doubtful if it is sufficiently different from other haemoglobins to necessitate the prefix, and like these it consists of four linked pyrrole rings joined to a central iron atom and attached to the protein globin. Produced at the same time as bacteroids are formed[551] it results in a red coloration of the infected region, where it has been located in soluble form between the bacteroids and host membrane[49] and has been shown to be associated with fixation.[544] Its possible significance in the symbiosis will be discussed later but it is worth mentioning at this point that the addition of haemoglobin to pure cultures of *Rhizobium* does not allow the bacterium to fix nitrogen.

2.4 The site of fixation within the nodules

The findings that the amount of nitrogen fixed at any one time was directly proportional to the volume of central infected tissue,[124,398,516] and to the haemoglobin content,[50,544] provided evidence that the site of fixation was within the infected cells. Studies to localize the fixation sites further have been carried out by Bergersen and Wilson.[49,58] They exposed soya bean nodules to ^{15}N, fractionated them by centrifugation and separated the three following fractions: a water-soluble fraction, a host plant membrane fraction which also contained a little bacteroid tissue, and the main bacteroid-containing fraction. Each fraction was then assayed for ^{15}N-enrichment, the following results being obtained: after 15 minutes the membrane fraction was most highly labelled, the water-soluble fraction was enriched to a lesser degree, while the bacteroid fraction showed no enrichment even after 2 hours. Furthermore, labelling of the membrane fraction decreased with time while that of the soluble fraction increased, suggesting transfer of ^{15}N from the membrane to the water-soluble fraction. Thus the site of fixation appears to be associated with the host plant membrane, although the bacteroid surface cannot be excluded. On the basis of the available data Bergersen[49] proposed the following hypothesis to explain the mechanism of fixation in legume nodules:

1. The host plant membrane is the site of fixation.

2. The bacteroids provide a source of reducing power which is transferred to the nitrogen-fixing membrane via haemoglobin which thus acts as an electron carrier. It has been shown that under anaerobic conditions molecular nitrogen can oxidize haemoglobin and there is evidence that the haemoglobin can be reduced by the bacteroids,[52,58,236] although other workers[325] could not confirm this. Evidence has been obtained to show that conditions in the nodules are sufficiently anaerobic to allow this process to occur even when the external partial pressure of oxygen is as high as 0.5 atm. (see 4.6).

3. The links between the bacteroids and haemoglobin, and haemoglobin and the membrane are uncertain, but it has been suggested that cytochromes, present on the plasma membrane of bacteroids,[174] may be involved in the transfer between the latter and the haemoglobin.

4. The host supplies photosynthetic products which act as substrates for the bacteroids and thus indirectly provide the source of reducing power. It also provides the carbon skeletons necessary before the ammonia formed by the reduction of nitrogen (see 8.3) can be converted to amino acids. No doubt it supplies energy as well. Bergersen's diagrammatic representation of his hypothesis is shown in Fig. 3.

A second view based on physico-chemical evidence has been proposed by Bauer,[37] who suggested that the two haem proteins into which haemoglobin can be separated by electrophoresis are the actual site of fixation, the nitrogen molecule becoming attached on to these and there combining with hydrogen. This theory has also been proposed to explain the effect of various gases on fixation (see 4.6). It has been elaborated by Abel[2] who observed that when haemoglobin is extracted under molecular hydrogen the haem groups complex with gaseous nitrogen rather than with oxygen,[4] that a change in configuration of the haem proteins occurs with increase in pH, and that increase in pH increases the binding properties of haemoglobin.[3] Taking these findings and other physico-chemical evidence into

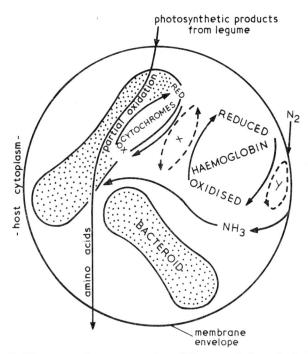

FIG. 3. Diagrammatic representation of Bergersen's hypothesis on the sequence of reactions in nitrogen-fixation by legume root nodules (see text). X represents unknown links in an electron transport chain between the bacteroid cytochromes and haemoglobin. Y represents unknown links between haemoglobin and the membrane envelope which is considered to be the site of conversion of molecular nitrogen to ammonia (after ref. 49).

consideration, Abel[2] has proposed the following main steps in the fixation process:

1. The nitrogen molecule becomes bound into a 'cradle' formed by the two haem proteins linked together (the ferro-enzyme), and there it gains two electrons, one from each iron atom, to give the ferri-enzyme. Hydrogen present in the surrounding medium reacts with the ferri-enzyme to give the ferro-enzyme and two protons which immediately combine with the nitrogen anion to give the diimide $(HN=NH)$.

2. To accommodate the larger size of the diimide, a change in configuration of the ferro-enzyme occurs. This is brought about by an increase in pH which accompanies the production and

liberation of molecular hydrogen from free protons in the system.

3. The diimide is then further reduced step by step, each step being accompanied by an increase in pH and a resulting change in configuration of the ferro-enzyme, until eventually two molecules of ammonia are produced. These being small in size escape from the cradle and are incorporated into general metabolism.

4. The ferro-enzyme is then converted back to its original configuration by a drop in pH resulting from the diffusion of protons into the system, and the process of fixation is repeated. The possible stages in this scheme, which could also explain the evolution of molecular hydrogen by nitrogen-fixing root nodules (see 4.6) can be represented as shown in Fig. 4.

This hypothesis does not explain where the site of fixation is in free-living organisms which apparently do not contain haemoglobin. Also the enzymes which convert hydrogen ions to molecular hydrogen (hydrogenase) and on which the nitrogen is reduced (nitrogenase) appear to be two distinct entities (see 8.7), not one as envisaged in this scheme.

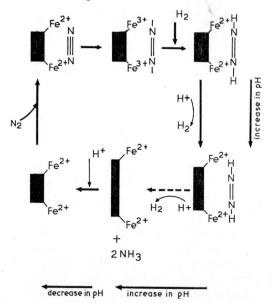

FIG. 4. Diagrammatic representation of Abel's hypothesis (see text).

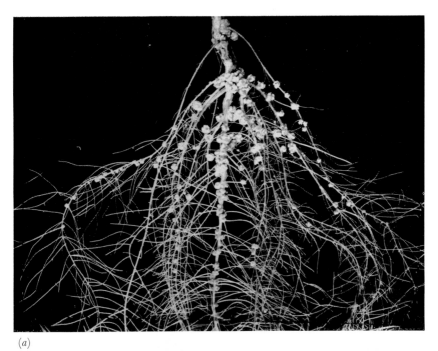

(a)

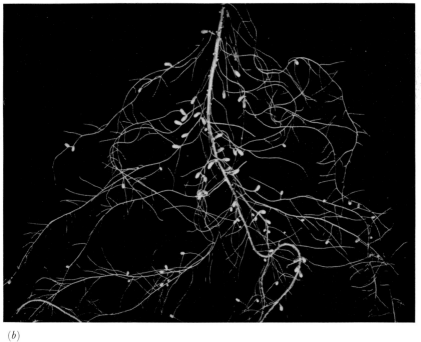

(b)

PLATE I: Typical effective nodules on the roots of (a) soya bean and (b) red clover. × I approx.

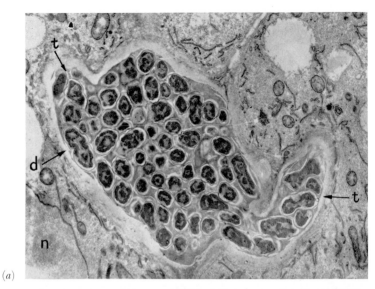

(a)

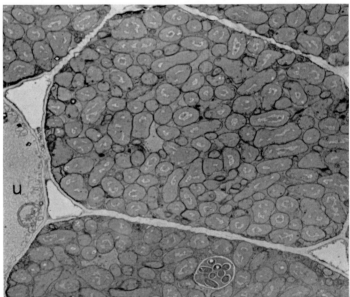

(b)

PLATE 2: (a) Two developing infection threads (t) arising from a group of rhizobial cells and penetrating two adjacent cells of a barrel medick nodule. One rhizobial cell is apparently dividing (d); (n) denotes host cell nucleus. ×7000. (b) Mature infected cells of a subterranean clover nodule filled with bacteroids. The lower cell contains an infection thread with rod-shaped bacteria. Note the increase in size which each bacterium undergoes as a result of bacteroid formation. (u) indicates an uninvaded cell. ×3000.

2.5 Rhizobia and nodule number

Although it had been suggested as early as 1858 by Lachmann[307] that bacteria caused nodule formation, Beijerinck,[45] as mentioned previously, was the first to isolate in pure culture a nodule bacterium and to show it was responsible for nodule formation. Nodule bacteria are free-living, aerobic, flagellated rods, approximately 1–3μ in length, and gram-negative in staining reaction. Their exact taxonomic position has been, and still is, a matter of diverse opinion, but suffice it to say that at present bacteria capable of inducing nodules on legume roots are placed in the genus *Rhizobium*, one of the three bacterial genera comprising the family Rhizobiaceae. Although aerobic, rhizobia grow well at partial pressures of oxygen as low as 0·01 atm.[36] and this may be important in relation to growth within the nodule where oxygen tensions are probably very low (see 4.6). It may be that cessation of bacterial multiplication within the nodules is due to the oxygen tension falling below a critical level. Rhizobial growth is optimal in the pH range 6·5–7·5[539] and various carbohydrates and nitrogen sources are readily used, but molecular nitrogen is not fixed. Growth factors are often stimulatory[388,564] and sometimes essential.[574]

Free-living rhizobia are of widespread occurrence in the soil and it can be assumed that if nodulated legumes are present in a particular habitat, bacteria capable of inducing nodule formation will also be present. Conversely in the absence of legumes rhizobial numbers in the soil decrease.[401] However although rhizobia may be present, specific strains capable of inducing nodulation on a particular species may not be, the rhizobia being specific in that they induce nodules on certain host plant species only. The bacterial strains which cause the formation of white, non-nitrogen-fixing nodules on a particular host are termed 'ineffective' in respect to that host, and rhizobia capable of inducing varying degrees of effective nodules are also known. Reports that ineffective strains can be converted to effective ones by repeated transfer through a particular host plant have seldom been confirmed using critical methods.[517,541] Why specificity between rhizobia and host exists is uncertain but there is good evidence that it is influenced by the genetic constitution of the latter.[392,395,397a]

Fred, Baldwin and McCoy recognized sixteen cross-inoculation groups of rhizobia, the members of which induce nodules on any one of a certain number of legume genera and on these only.[201] Specific rank was given to the rhizobia of six of these as follows: *Rhizobium japonicum* (soya bean group), *R. leguminosarum* (pea group), *R. lupini* (lupin group), *R. meliloti* (alfalfa group), *R. phaseoli* (bean group) and *R. trifolii* (clover group). It is of interest that these are the rhizobia of agriculturally important plant species and thus the most extensively studied. Generally the cross-inoculation groups are quite restrictive but work by J. K. Wilson[576-8] was probably the first to suggest that the cross-inoculation groups were not as clear-cut as once thought. He suggested that promiscuity between rhizobia and host plants is common, but this is contrary to the views and findings of most other workers. There are however some undoubted records of nodules being formed on legumes by rhizobia from other host plant groupings. For example rhizobia from pea and clover have been shown to cross-inoculate to produce a few ineffective nodules.[297a] Mutation of effective to ineffective rhizobia, after exposure to x-rays,[287] or treatment with bacteriophage,[297] has also been noted, and recent evidence of transduction in bacteria may explain what have appeared in the past to be rather incredible findings.

Early workers suggested that the number of nodules formed per plant was almost entirely dependent on the number of rhizobia added in an inoculum. It now seems clear that this is really not so, for if suitable conditions exist in the soil, the rhizobia multiply extremely quickly[513] and maximum values are generally obtained at least 3 days before nodulation commences.[434] On the contrary when rhizobia are abundant the nodule mass is determined by the host plant. It has been shown that there is an almost linear relationship between nodule and lateral root numbers per plant[393] and that plants with strongly developed tap roots and few lateral roots nodulate less abundantly than do those with numerous fibrous roots.[396,398] These and similar findings support the theory proposed by Nutman[393] that the sites of nodule initiation are similar to those of lateral root primordia and that nodules may be formed instead of lateral roots. Other workers have suggested that the association between rooting habit and nodulation is coincidental.[6a] The total mass of nodules formed on any host strain is more or less constant providing sufficient time is allowed for this to become established. This is because the first-formed nodules produce an inhibitory substance which prevents other nodules forming near them. This can be demonstrated by removing existing nodules for then further nodules develop, but only until the original nodule yield has been re-established.[394] The inhibitory substance is produced in the nodule apex and large nodules exert a greater inhibitory effect than do small ones.[394] Ineffective nodules do not produce an inhibitory substance and this may explain why, when formed, they are present in much larger numbers than effective ones. Recent studies on the rhizobia have been reviewed by Allen and Allen,[7] while the interrelations between rhizobia and host plant have been expertly summarized by Nutman.[396,398-9,401]

3 Symbiotic Nitrogen Fixation
II. Non-Legumes

3.1

The ability of nodulated plants to fix nitrogen is not a prerogative of the Leguminosae only. There is in addition a group of non-leguminous angiosperms, the root nodules of which fix nitrogen as efficiently as do those of legumes. Despite this, these plants have received scant attention in the past. In recent years however, largely as a result of the work of the Glasgow school under Bond[75-6,80] their importance as vigorous nitrogen fixers is at last being appreciated.

These plants, all of which are woody perennials, bear laterally on their roots nodules inhabited not by a *Rhizobium*, but probably by filamentous bacteria (actinomycetes). These microorganisms must be of widespread occurrence in the soil, as they are not seed-borne and yet field material of non-legumes, at least in Britain, is generally nodulated. Although variously interpreted in the past, the nodules appear to be modified lateral roots without root hairs. Those of several genera: *Alnus, Casuarina, Myrica*[75] and *Coriaria*[488] develop a red coloration, which appears to be due to the presence of anthocyanin.[70] Its function is uncertain but there is no evidence that it has any connexion with the nitrogen-fixing capacity of the nodules. The plants are world-wide in distribution and characteristic of habitats of low nitrogen status, as can be seen from Table 1 in which the known genera are listed. It is probable that other nitrogen-fixing plants of similar type remain to be discovered.

3.2 Tests for nitrogen fixation

The ability of nodulated non-legumes to fix nitrogen was first suggested, as mentioned previously, by Nobbe and his co-workers in 1892.[389] They showed that nodulated plants of

TABLE 1. The geographical distribution and common ecological habitats of nitrogen-fixing non-legumes

Genus	Distribution (after ref. 80)	Habitat
Alnus	North temperate and arctic regions; South America, Japan	River banks, mountain slopes
Casuarina	Tropical Asia, Australia, Pacific islands	Coastal soils and dune systems
Ceanothus	North America	Forest soils, particularly newly cleared areas
Comptonia	North America	Undergrowth of forests
Coriaria	Southern Europe and Southern Asia; North Africa and South America; New Zealand	Pioneer plants on eroded and newly cleared soils
Discaria	Australasia, South America	Stony plains
Elaeagnus	Asia, Europe, North America	Eroded slopes, overgrazed pastures
Hippophaë	Temperate and Arctic regions of Europe and Asia	Coastal areas, near inland waters
Myrica	Tropical to sub-Arctic regions	Acid bog-land, mountain regions in tropics
Shepherdia	North America	Sandy soils, eroded slopes, near water courses

Elaeagnus angustifolia grew healthily in pot culture in the absence of combined nitrogen, whereas non-nodulated plants did not, and that better growth occurred only after nodules had developed. Similar experiments, showing the ability of nodulated plants to increase not only their growth but also their nitrogen contents in nitrogen-free media, have provided evidence of fixation by *Ceanothus, Elaeagnus, Coriaria, Shepherdia, Alnus, Casuarina, Hippophaë* and *Myrica*. (For references see the reviews by Bond.[75-6,80]) The suggestion that nodules were the actual nitrogen-fixing sites was made by Hiltner[261] who reported in 1904 that *Alnus* failed to make satisfactory growth in nitrogen-free solution if the nodules were excised as they appeared.[390a] The nitrogen-fixing function of the nodules has been confirmed unequivocally for the above-mentioned genera, and for *Discaria*[354] and *Comptonia*[609] using detached nodules and ^{15}N-labelled molecular nitrogen.

Fixation per unit dry weight of nodule tissue is greatest in the young nodules and decreases with age, this being due presumably to the development of an increasing proportion of cork and xylem which contributes nothing to fixation. On detachment non-legume nodules lose their powers of fixation, but not so quickly as do those of legumes. In the legume soya bean, for example, little fixation occurred 6 hours after detachment,[104] whereas in non-legume nodules it continues much longer, particularly in *Hippophaë*, where fixation still occurs 24 hours after excision (Fig. 5).[74] This is probably because non-legume nodules contain a greater supply of respiratory substrates than do

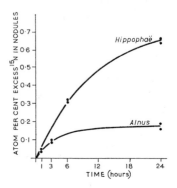

FIG. 5. Assimilation of ^{15}N-enriched molecular nitrogen by detached nodules of *Alnus* and *Hippophaë* (after ref. 74).

their legume counterparts. These results, together with the finding that the nodule endophyte, at least in *Alnus*, is several times more efficient in fixation per unit weight than is the free-living bacterium *Azotobacter* under optimum conditions,[490] indicate why non-legume nodules are superior to those of legumes for studies on detached nodules, and why they may also prove to be more useful than those of legumes for the preparation of nitrogen-fixing cell-free extracts.

3.3 Nodule initiation and structure

There is no record which has been independently confirmed that the nodule endophyte has been isolated, neither is it seed borne. Inoculation must therefore be carried out in the laboratory by applying a suspension of crushed nodules to the root systems, or by growing the plants in soil where the organism is indigenous.

Nodules, which appear to arise from single infection points, become visible about 10 to 21 days after inoculation. Distortion of the root hairs is associated with infection, as in the legumes, but, because of the crude inocula used, cannot be said with certainty to be caused by the actual endophyte. Unlike those of the majority of legumes, the root hairs frequently branch. The endophyte, according to evidence presented by Taubert[509] and Pommer,[422] enters the root hair, and traverses the cortex in the form of a hypha or naked protoplasmic thread. Few workers have been able to distinguish a micro-organism within the root hairs, and it has been accepted more from analogy with legumes rather than from visual observation that the root hairs are the initial sites of infection. The origin of the tissues comprising the nodules is uncertain. In *Myrica gale* the earliest stage which has been distinguished in the initiation of the nodule is the formation of a spherical mass of meristematic cells enclosed in the parent-root endodermis, and which has arisen from the pericycle. This mass eventually develops an apical meristem and a central vascular cylinder which links up with that of the main root. At this stage the endophyte can be seen in the basal cortical region of the nodule.[182] Thus, the origin is similar to that of a lateral root. A similar finding has been reported by Taubert[509] for *Alnus* nodules, but a slightly different origin for nodules of the latter genus has been recorded by Pommer.[422] He observed that meristematic division of infected cortical cells first occurs as in legumes, the area then becoming almost completely enclosed in a periderm. This is followed by the production of a lateral root which becomes modified and links up with the infected cortical tissue, both growing out to form the nodule, still largely enclosed in the periderm layer. Thus according to Pommer, the nodule comprises both lateral root tissue and cortical tissue of the parent root. It is not known whether meristematic activity and infection in non-legumes is associated with the presence of tetraploid cells. Quispel considers that the nodules arise at distinct foci on the root, but that these are not the foci of normal lateral root initiation.[436] Although unbranched in the young stage the apical meristem of the nodule later branches repeatedly resulting in a perennial coralloid mass, as can be seen in Plate 3a (opposite p. 38) which shows typical field nodules of *Alnus glutinosa*.

The mature nodules, which range in diameter from a few millimetres to more than 15 cm, are covered with a thick cork layer except at the white, actively growing, branch tips. A curious feature of *Myrica* and *Casuarina* nodules is the presence of a white, negatively geotropic rootlet which develops at the tip of each nodule lobe 2–3 weeks after the nodules become apparent. These rootlets, which are generally unbranched, may account for a large proportion of the total root tissue per plant, as can be seen from the *Myrica* root system shown in Plate 3b (opposite p. 38). Internally they show a typical root structure except that they contain numerous air spaces in the cortex. The latter, unlike that of the nodules, is not infected. Early in development the nodules become almost completely covered in a thick cork layer without lenticels so that it is likely that these roots are aerating in function.[71] Such a function would undoubtedly be an asset to *Myrica gale* in the water-logged conditions in which it typically grows, but they are also characteristic of other *Myrica* species from a variety of habitats. The negative geotropism of the nodule roots may be related to their endogenous IAA concentration. In *Myrica* and *Casuarina*, both of which bear negatively geotropic roots, no endogenous IAA could be detected in the nodules, although it was abundant in *Alnus* nodules which have no nodule roots and in which the ordinary roots show positive geotropism.[470] This appears to be due to the nodules of the former two genera having a high IAA-binding capacity and an active IAA-oxidase system. It has been suggested[470] that this results in IAA concentrations on the lower side of the nodule roots being more nearly optimal than on the upper side so that negative geotropism results. It is of interest to note that although *Alnus* and *Myrica* are often found in similar habitats, the *Alnus* nodules, unlike those of *Myrica*, often occur at, or near, the soil surface and have lenticels present in the cork layer.[180] Therefore for *Alnus* a special aerating mechanism is less important.

Thus externally the nodules are rather distinct from those of the legumes. What now of their internal anatomy? All non-legume nodules are characterized by showing in tranverse section an outer well-developed cork layer, an endophyte-containing cortex and a central stele which develops secondary thickening. The position of the infected region within the cortex varies with the genus, but not all genera, far less all species, have been critically examined. In *Alnus* the infected cells form concentric zones, several of which may be present in old nodules, but young nodules contain only one. In *Myrica* the endophyte is found scattered throughout the cortex,[182,469] while in *Ceanothus* the infected region comprises the middle or outer cortex.[208] Thus the presence of the endophyte in the cortex contrasts very markedly with the infected region of legume nodules which is internal to the vascular system (compare Fig. 2*e*, p. 18, and Fig. 6, p. 32).

The infected cells of non-legume nodules are large and may be devoid of all,[44] or almost all,[469] host cell contents. In those of certain genera such as *Alnus* and *Ceanothus* the endophyte may form densely packed globular or club-shaped vesicles which are believed to be reproductive in function.[208,246] The non-infected cells remain small, and become filled with starch and tannins. Sections through *Alnus* and *Myrica* nodules are shown in Plate 4*a* (opposite p. 40) and Fig. 6 respectively. In longitudinal section the cortex of non-legume nodules can be divided into three zones: nearest the apical meristem is the youngest which comprises newly infected tissue; this gives way to a zone of mature infected cells, and then to a region of degenerate infected cells. According to Schaede[459] digestion of the endophyte and absorption of the digested products by surrounding cells is a mechanism whereby fixed nitrogen is transferred from the nodule to the remainder of the plant but Stewart found no evidence of this in first-year alder plants.[490]

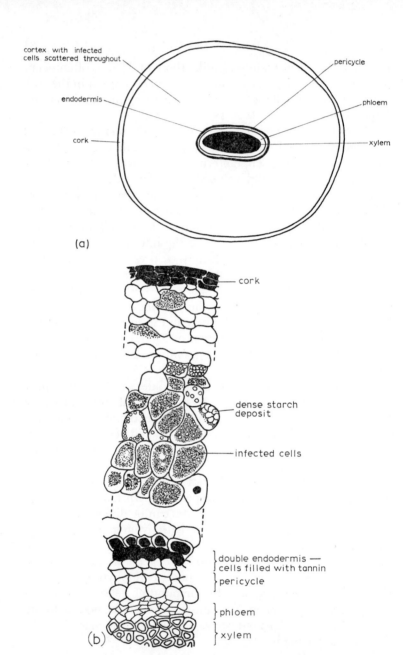

FIG. 6. T.S. Nodule lobe of *Myrica gale* showing (a) arrangement of tissues (×40) and (b) cells as seen under H.P. (×330).

3.4 The identity and nature of the endophyte

This has been a problem since the days of early investigators such as Woronin,[604] and even today the exact taxonomic position of the endophyte is still not known with certainty, although advances in our understanding have been made. The problem has been attacked from two main angles: from a study of the cytology of the endophyte as it occurs within the nodules, and from a study of organisms isolated from the nodules.

Cytological studies have provided good descriptions of many of the features of non-legume nodules[7,80] but the chief difficulty has been in interpreting the nature of the structures observed under the light microscope. Most recent advances in the identification of the endophyte have been made with the aid of electron microscopy and it appears that in *Myrica cerifera*[469] and *Alnus glutinosa*[44,211] the nodule endophyte is almost certainly a filamentous bacterium or actinomycete. It thus shows characteristics intermediate between the true fungi and true bacteria. This confirms similar suggestions made on the basis of light microscope studies by earlier workers.[182,459] In both species the endophyte is seen as a fine, branched, septate structure. In *Myrica* it is approximately $1\ \mu$ in diameter,[469] in *Alnus* it has been reported as being $0 \cdot 2 – 0 \cdot 5\ \mu$[44] and $0 \cdot 7 – 1 \cdot 0\ \mu$[211] in diameter. The diameter of the hyphae and lack of a nuclear membrane within the filaments are two of the main criteria used in attributing the endophytes of non-legumes to the actinomycetes. It traverses the cortex and appears to penetrate the cells non-mechanically.[469] According to Becking and his co-workers[44] the hyphae of the *Alnus* endophyte comprise: (1) a central area probably of nuclear material, (2) cytoplasm which contains membraneous-like bodies (probably plasmalemmosomes[164]), (3) a cytoplasmic membrane, and (4) a hyphal cell wall. This is surrounded possibly by a mucilage layer, and eventually by a membrane system which is probably the invaginated plasmalemma of the host cell, as in legumes (see 2.3). In the infected cells of *Alnus*, the vesicles, so typical under the light microscope (Plate 4*b*, opposite p. 39), are seen to be terminal cells of hyphae, $3–4\ \mu$ in diameter and with numerous compartments and a complex membrane system. Such findings have in general been confirmed independently.[211] An additional stage in which the hyphae fragment to form bacteroid-like cells has also been seen, this fragmentation of the hyphae being characteristic of free-living actinomycetes such as *Nocardia*. These bacteroid-like cells (seen clearly in Plate 5*a*, opposite p. 54) are very reminiscent of the bacteroids seen in, and associated with nitrogen fixation in legume nodules. However, according to Becking *et al.*[44] they are formed only in dead host cells and may eventually form structures which may be resting spores. Gardner, on the other hand, has recently reported that rather similar bacteroid-like cells (Plate 5*b* opposite p. 54) are present in metabolically active cells of *Alnus*, and that these are most frequent in the nodules in spring and summer, while vesicles are most abundant in winter.[211] It is thus possible that the bacteroid stage may be associated with fixation as in legumes, although no conclusive proof that this is so has yet been obtained.

The ease of isolation of legume rhizobia suggested that the isolation of non-legume endophytes would be a routine procedure, but, as can be judged from the studies of the Japanese worker Uemura,[527-8] who isolated numerous organisms from *Alnus* nodules and found none which satisfy Koch's postulates, the opposite appears to be the case. Many organisms, including *Rhizobium*-like species, have been isolated by earlier workers and claimed to be endophytes, but because of the unsatisfactory methodology (small numbers of plants employed, inadequate controls etc.), only the most recent claims—those of Pommer[423] and Niewiarowska[386-7] deserve serious attention.[80] Pommer isolated on glucose-asparagine agar an actinomycete-like organism from alder nodules which induced nodulation in as little as 3 weeks of re-infection. Similar organisms were also isolated from *Elaeagnus*, *Hippophaë* and *Shepherdia* nodules. Quispel also working on *Alnus* has been unable to confirm Pommer's results and has obtained evidence that an alcohol extract of alder roots is necessary for growth of the endophyte.[437] To reconcile these views it has been suggested that the endophyte may exist in different forms, and that these forms have different growth requirements.[437] As mentioned above Gardner has obtained evidence that the morphological forms within the *Alnus* nodule show some seasonal variation. Niewiarowska isolated from *Hippophaë* nodules an actinomycete, probably a species of *Nocar-*

dia, which in large-scale experiments effected nodulation on re-infection, but aseptic techniques were not employed.

A possible way of finding out whether the endophytes of these various species and genera are similar is to see whether they cross-inoculate. If they do it is likely that a similar endophyte is present in the genera or species tested; if they do not it is probable that the endophytes are quite distinct. Cross-inoculation of certain genera is known to occur, for example *Hippophaë*, *Elaeagnus* and *Shepherdia* cross-inoculate[212] while others, for example, *Alnus* and *Myrica* do not.[182] It seems likely therefore, from the results accumulated to date, that although each genus may not have a specific endophyte, cross-inoculation occurs only between genera of the same family. It has also been suggested that more than one organism is necessary for nodulation to occur.[527]

3.5 The site of fixation within the nodules

There is little doubt that in young non-legume nodules the amount of nitrogen fixed is proportional to the volume of infected tissue and that the site of fixation is within the infected cells. There is no evidence that the upwardly growing rootlets characteristic of *Myrica* and *Casuarina* fix nitrogen. The question as to where fixation occurs within the infected cell is still unanswered. If it is intracellular to the endophyte this would necessitate a continuous lysis of the endophyte, a view for which there is no evidence, or a continuous excretion by the endophyte of the nitrogen fixed. It is difficult to conceive of an organism continuously excreting approximately 90 per cent of the nitrogen fixed as the *Alnus* endophyte would have to do, as this proportion of the nitrogen fixed is continuously transferred from the nodules.[490]

It is more reasonable to assume that the site of fixation is extracellular to the endophyte as in legumes, where it is thought to be associated with haemoglobin,[2,37] or with haemoglobin and the membrane system enclosing the bacteroids.[49] A spectroscopic examination for the presence of haemoglobin in non-legume nodules is difficult because they contain a strong phenoloxidase system which causes rapid discolouration of the nodules when they are crushed.[138] Earlier workers failed to detect the pigment[165,479-80] but it is now established that nodules of *Alnus*, *Myrica*, *Hippophaë* and *Casuarina* have haematin contents several times greater than in the cortex of non-nodulated roots, and that *Casuarina* does in fact contain a pigment which if oxygenated and de-oxygenated shows similar absorption bands to haemo-globin under similar conditions. As it also contains iron in the ferrous state it seems likely that it is haemoglobin.[138] It is probable that a similar type of pigment is present in *Myrica* and *Alnus* and that it is firmly attached to cellular material rather than free in solution as in legumes.[138] Membranes of host plant origin surround the endophyte as in legumes,[44] so that the hypo-thesis of Bergersen that the membrane is the site of fixation in legumes can probably be applied to non-legume nodules as well.

3.6 Root nodules of other plants

Although the nitrogen-fixing capacity of the non-legume nod-ules mentioned above is well established, there are in addition certain other groups of higher plants the nodules of which have been reported to fix nitrogen.

Evidence has been obtained that the gymnosperm *Podocarpus* fixes nitrogen. This genus comprises approximately two hundred species presently distributed throughout the southern hemi-sphere, although it was formerly present in the northern hemi-sphere also, for example, it has been recorded in the Tertiary flora in Scotland.[473] The plants are characteristic of poor soils and the nodules occur closely adpressed together in two rows along the length of the roots. It was suggested by early work-ers[390,482] that the nodules fixed nitrogen but Bond, using the critical ^{15}N technique and material from European botanic gardens, could not confirm this.[77] Recently however evidence of fixation by detached field nodules has been obtained using the ^{15}N method.[57] It has also been shown that, as in legume nodules, hydrogen is evolved during the fixation process, indicat-ing that a hydrogenase system is present. Unlike the nodulated angiosperms described above, the fixation rates were low and appreciable ^{15}N-enrichment was detected only by exposing the nodules to molecular nitrogen highly enriched with ^{15}N and by analysing the acid-soluble fraction. The low fixation rates were attributed in part to the fact that in the bulked samples analysed only a small proportion of the nodules contained an endophyte[57] and it may be that in the European material previously examined an effective endophyte was not present. The nature of the micro-organism present in *Podocarpus* nodules is uncertain, but it has been variously identified as a bacterium[335] or as a fungus.[456] Should the latter identification prove correct *Podocarpus* will be the first nodulated plant containing a fungal endophyte in which fixation has been established. Certain other gymnosperms, for example *Ceratozamia* and *Encephalartos*, bear nodules inhabited by nitrogen-fixing blue-green algae but in these fixation is not dependent on a symbiotic association for the free-living algae also fix nitrogen. These are considered later (see 5.7).

Among the angiosperms there is some evidence that certain members of the Zygophyllaceae (*Zygophyllum*, *Fagonia*, and *Tribulus*) fix nitrogen. In this family of xerophytic shrubs it has been reported that certain Egyptian species, which bear nodules on the roots, and on stems in contact with the soil, grow healthily in sterilized sand whereas non-nodulated plants do not. On this basis it has been suggested that the nodules fix nitrogen.[453] Bacteroids very similar to those of legumes were reported in the nodules and the endophytes were considered rhizobia-like. Micro-organisms isolated from the nodules of the three genera were not seed-borne and did not cross-inoculate, although they nodulated certain legumes.[367] However in a critical study of the nodules of *Tribulus cistoides*, Allen and Allen found no cytological evidence of an endophyte, neither could they isolate one.[6] They suggested that in fact the structures were probably starch storage organs, and that they were morphologically dissimilar both to the nodules of the legumes and non-legumes such as *Alnus*.[7] Root nodules have been recorded recently in the families, Rosaceae (*Dryas drummondii*),[8,131,309] and Ericaceae (*Arctostaphylos uva-ursi*)[8] but these have not been tested for nitrogen fixation, although it seems likely on the basis of ecological data that *Dryas drummondii* fixes nitrogen.[131] Other nodulated Rosaceous species which appear to fix nitrogen have been described recently. These are, *Cercocarpus betuloides*,[553] and two important browse species in the eastern United States, *Purschia tridentata* and *P. glandulosa*.[554a] It is desirable that the nitrogen-fixing capacity of the nodules of these plants be examined using the ^{15}N technique.

(a)

(b)

PLATE 3: (a) Typical root nodules on field material of *Alnus glutinosa*. ×½. (b) The root system of a ten week old *Myrica gale* plant showing the presence of upwardly growing nodule roots. ×⅔.

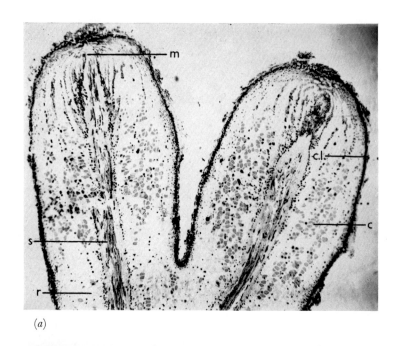

(a)

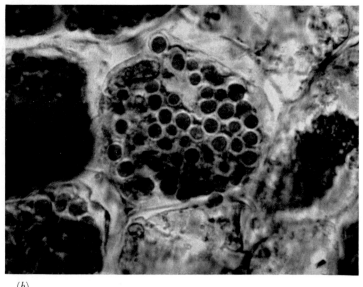

(b)

PLATE 4: (a) R.L.S. through a branched nodule of *Alnus glutinosa* showing the meristem (m), cork layer (c.l.), stele (s), cortex with dark stained infected cells (c) and region where infected cells have disappeared (r). × 30. (b) Infected cells of an *Alnus glutinosa* nodule filled with dark stained spherical vesicles. × 1250.

4 Symbiotic Nitrogen Fixation
III. Physiology

4.1

Studies on the physiology of symbiotic nitrogen fixation have been carried out largely at the 'whole-plant' level and there are at least two good reasons for this. In the first instance it is important to consider the factors affecting the symbiosis as it exists naturally, and secondly there has been little alternative, because it is not yet possible to obtain nitrogen-fixing fractions with prolonged activity, or to obtain consistently, nitrogen-fixing cell-free extracts. Thus, it is sometimes difficult to ensure that the results obtained are due to a direct effect on fixation, rather than to an indirect effect associated with the overall growth of the legume or of the rhizobia. Information on the actual mechanism of fixation in symbiotic systems has therefore lagged behind that obtained for free-living micro-organisms from which nitrogen-fixing cell-free extracts are now readily available. On the other hand, more information on the physiology of symbiotic plants has been accumulated than on the physiology of any other group of nitrogen-fixing organisms.

The rates at which nodulated legumes and non-legumes assimilate elemental nitrogen are affected not only by the efficiency of the nitrogen-fixing mechanism in the plant *per se* but also by the degree of effective nodulation. Studies to date have shown that both fixation and nodulation are influenced by many physical, chemical, and nutritional factors, and some of the results obtained have provided glimpses of the nitrogen-fixing pathways in these organisms.

4.2 The effect of combined nitrogen on fixation and the importance of the carbohydrate : nitrogen ratio

The inhibitory effect of high levels of combined nitrogen on nitrogen fixation by nodulated plants is a characteristic feature.[18,498] Generally the higher the level of available combined nitrogen the less nitrogen that is fixed, although very small quantities may sometimes result in an increase, because of the increased overall vigour of the plants. As a typical example we may consider data obtained by Stewart and Bond using ^{15}N on the effect of combined nitrogen on nitrogen fixation and nodulation in *Alnus glutinosa* (Table 2). It is evident from the growth

TABLE 2. The effect of ammonium-nitrogen on growth, nitrogen fixation and nodulation of *Alnus glutinosa* (after ref. 498)

	Ammonium-nitrogen added (mg per litre)	0	10	50	100
1. Growth and nitrogen data	Mean total plant weight (mg)	3,123	6,677	9,257	10,634
	Mean total nitrogen per plant (mg)	63	130	174	208
	Mean mg elemental nitrogen assimilated	63	99	69	49
	Elemental nitrogen fixed as percentage of total nitrogen per plant	100	77	39	24
2. Nodulation data	Mean total dry weight of nodules (mg)	144	243	230	158
	Mean nodule number	64	69	32	25
	Nodule weight as percentage of total plant weight	4·6	3·6	2·5	1·5
3. Nodule efficiency data	Mg nitrogen fixed per gm nodule dry matter	438	410	315	310

and nitrogen data (1) that although the total amounts of nitrogen assimilated increases with increase in available combined nitrogen, the percentage contribution of elemental nitrogen markedly decreases. This is because: First, as can be seen from the nodule data (2), nodule weight as a percentage of total plant weight decreases with increase in combined nitrogen. Secondly, as the nodule efficiency data (3) show, the nodules which do form in the presence of combined nitrogen are less efficient in fixation than are those formed in the absence of combined nitrogen. Thus considerable quantities of combined nitrogen reduce the number of root infections, or infections which ultimately develop into nodules, and the nodules which do form are of reduced importance to the plant, which bases its nitrogen metabolism largely on combined nitrogen. Typical plants of *Alnus glutinosa* and *Myrica gale* grown in the presence of various levels of combined nitrogen are shown in Plate 6 (opposite p. 55).

The type of combined nitrogen supplied to the plants is of some importance in that nitrate-nitrogen inhibits nodulation to a greater extent than does ammonium-nitrogen.[546] Even so, the levels necessary to inhibit nodulation and fixation markedly appear to be greater than those generally occurring in the field, so that there it is likely that nitrogen fixation will occur. Perhaps the best evidence that this is so is the widespread gains in nitrogen which occur in soils where legumes and nodulated non-legumes grow (see 9.3 and 9.4).

The inhibition of fixation by ammonium-nitrogen can be readily explained if it is accepted that elemental nitrogen is first reduced to ammonia at the nitrogen-fixing sites in the nodule prior to amino acid synthesis (see 8.3), but why it also affects nodulation is less certain. Several theories have been advanced with particular reference to the legumes, but all could apply equally to the non-legumes. Allison and Ludwig,[15] who reviewed the earlier of these, proposed that nodule reduction was a concomitant of reduced total root growth. While there is no doubt that root growth is reduced, nodulation is reduced to a greater extent,[520] so that some other factor must be operative. Thus Wilson,[580] on the basis of accumulated evidence, proposed that the degree of nodulation and nitrogen fixation by a plant is governed by its internal carbohydrate : nitrogen ratio. That is, each plant has a critical carbohydrate : nitrogen ratio, deviation from which results in sub-optimal nodulation and fixation. In addition to accounting for the well established fact that combined nitrogen inhibits nodulation and fixation the carbohydrate : nitrogen hypothesis may explain findings such as the following:

1. If the overall carbohydrate status of a plant is increased, for example by adding an exogenous carbohydrate source,[15] by increasing the light intensity,[592] period of illumination,[267] or carbon dioxide supply,[216,592] the inhibitory effect of combined nitrogen is decreased. At the same time an excessive supply of carbohydrate also inhibits nodulation and fixation.

2. On detachment, nodules rapidly stop fixing nitrogen. This indicates a requirement for host plant substrates, probably carbohydrates, as is evidenced by the fact that fixation by detached nodules can often be stimulated by supplying exogenous carbohydrates,[33] or by leaving a small part of the root system attached to the nodules.[78] Failure of carbohydrate to affect fixation may in some cases be due to its inability to penetrate the nodules quickly enough.

3. Nodules detached from plants previously placed in the dark retain their nitrogen-fixing activity for a shorter period than do those from light-grown plants.[552]

4. Some plants produce few, or no nodules in the dark, unless an exogenous carbohydrate supply is available.[463]

There can be no doubt on the basis of the above evidence that, directly, or indirectly, the carbohydrate : nitrogen ratio greatly influences nitrogen fixation and nodulation.

At the same time evidence has accumulated that other internal and external factors are also operative. For example, nodule shedding and degeneration is stimulated by flowering and fruiting[575] and can be delayed by removing the flower buds,[412] indicating that there is an internal hormonal effect. It may of course simply be that abscission results in a better supply of available nutrients for the nodules. It is of interest to note in connexion with a possible hormonal effect that in non-nodulated soya bean plants high levels of auxin in the plant and concomitant reduced root growth are associated with high levels of available combined nitrogen.[571] There is also evidence that combined nitrogen exerts external effects. For example, Gaumann, Jaag and Roth,[214] who investigated the effect of nitrate-nitrogen on a divided root system, part of which was treated with nitrate while the other part was not, found that the combined nitrogen affected nodulation only on that part of the root in direct contact with the nitrate-nitrogen.[214] This finding, and that of Thornton[518] who observed that nitrate-nitrogen inhibits root-hair curling in legumes, may possibly be explained by the recent finding[505] that nitrate-nitrogen inhibits the conversion by rhizobia of tryptophan to IAA, which is considered to be a precursor of root-hair infection (see 2.3). It may also explain why nitrate-nitrogen inhibits nodulation to a greater extent than does ammonium-nitrogen.[546]

Thus, summarizing the available data, it is apparent that the carbohydrate : nitrogen ratio and other internal factors, possibly including growth substances, affect nodulation and fixation. It seems reasonable to assume that in these nitrogen-fixing symbioses there exists an intricate system, in which the main function of the host plant is to supply a source of reducing power, carbon skeletons for amino acid synthesis, and probably an energy source for fixation. It has been suggested that the host also supplies a specific photosynthetic product necessary for nodulation to occur, but the success of several workers[35,98, 438-9] in obtaining nodules on excised roots cannot be easily reconciled with this view. However, even in experiments with excised roots the possibility of photosynthetic products being carried over in the seeds and made available to the root tips cannot be ruled out. For example, Bunting and Horrocks[98] achieved better nodulation in excised roots of large-seeded plants than in small-seeded ones.

A phenomenon associated with the carbohydrate : nitrogen ratio of the plant is the excretion of fixed nitrogen from nodulated roots. The suggestion that root excretion by legumes occurred was first made by Lipmann in 1912,[323] and was followed up by other workers, particularly by the Helsinki school under Virtanen.[540,551] They showed that excretion by legumes was a common phenomenon in the Helsinki laboratory, the excreted nitrogen generally accounting for 10 to 20 per cent, but sometimes for as much as 50 per cent, of the total nitrogen fixed.[547] It comprised mainly amino-nitrogen, of which aspartic and glutamic acids were dominant.[549-50] Workers elsewhere were unable to detect excreted compounds in their cultures (for references see Wilson[580] and Virtanen and Miettinen)[551] but

Wilson, who detected none in his laboratory at Madison, Wisconsin,[588] obtained excretion in experiments carried out during a visit to Helsinki. On returning to Madison similar experiments to those carried out in Finland were set up, but still no excretion was obtained, and the differences in results were attributed to differences in climatic conditions.[580] Factors such as daylength were then varied and eventually excretion was detected at Madison also. The phenomenon has been explained on the basis that if the photosynthetic rate is low insufficient nitrogen is fixed for excretion to occur; if on the contrary it is too high, all the nitrogen fixed is used up in cell synthesis. Only when the photosynthetic rate is such as to ensure good fixation without the formation of excess carbohydrate does fixation slightly exceed the needs of the plant and the nitrogen is excreted into the rooting medium.[580] It appears therefore to be a mechanism whereby the plants can get rid of excess fixed nitrogen and thus maintain a favourable internal carbohydrate : nitrogen ratio. Various other reports of the production of numerous and varied extracellular products by roots have appeared in the literature,[448] but it has not always been confirmed that these were derived by a process of excretion, rather than by cell autolysis, root decay etc.

4.3 The transfer of fixed nitrogen to the host plant

If the function of the endophyte complex within the nodules is to supply fixed nitrogen to the host plant, it is important to consider the mechanism whereby the nitrogen is transferred from the site of fixation to the remainder of the plant. From mere contemplation of the growth of a young nodulated plant in nitrogen-free medium it is evident that such a transfer begins early and is on a considerable scale throughout the active growth of the plant. How then does the transfer occur?

One theory is that the fixed nitrogen becomes available when the ageing endophyte is digested by the infected cells.[199,459] However evidence obtained by Bond[69] and subsequently by other workers for legumes,[411,590] and by Stewart[490] for non-legumes, shows that from the very start of fixation approximately 80–90 per cent of the total nitrogen fixed is rapidly transferred from the nodules to the remainder of the plant, and as there is no evidence for digestion of the endophyte during the early stages of growth, cell lysis cannot be responsible for the transfer. It is evident, for example from studies with alder, that relative to dry weight and nitrogen content the young nodules are most active in fixation.[490] Furthermore, if transfer was due to lysis in legumes, high proteolytic activity would be expected in the nodules, yet they are inactive in this respect.[548] Also, rapid multiplication of the bacteroids would be necessary to compensate for autolysis, and yet they appear incapable of multiplication.[580] The second theory is that the nitrogen is fixed by the endophyte and then excreted, but as noted on p. 35 this appears unlikely. The third theory is that the site of fixation is external to the endophyte.[49,545] This latter theory accords with the finding that rapid transfer from the sites of fixation does occur, and in view of the lack of cytological evidence for early digestion, appears more likely.

Once it was established that rapid transfer of nitrogen from the nitrogen-fixing sites occurs, the questions remained: how it is transferred, and in what form? Studies on *Alnus*[72] and *Hippophaë*[81] provided information on the first aspect. In these experiments a short zone of tissues external to the xylem was removed from the base of the shoot, the nodules exposed to ^{15}N-labelled gaseous nitrogen, and the rate of transfer of fixed nitrogen into the upper parts of the shoot then compared with that in non-ringed plants. It was found in *Alnus* that after 6 hours exposure to ^{15}N the shoot system was substantially enriched with the isotope and that there was no significant difference in the enrichment of ringed and unringed shoots, indicating that transfer of fixed nitrogen from the nodules to the remainder of the plant occurs via the xylem. The transfer of fixed nitrogen within the nodule from the site of fixation to the xylem is probably also via the transpiration stream in the case of annual nodules which can absorb water. In perennial nodules, such as those of the non-legumes where, because of the thick cork covering, there is little water absorption,[72] the material is possibly transferred to the xylem in water released into the nodules by the phloem and then conveyed out through the xylem.

The form in which the fixed nitrogen is transferred in legumes has been investigated by various workers. Pate and Wallace[414] studied the rate of exudation of nitrogenous compounds from excised root systems of *Pisum arvense* and found, as can be seen from Fig. 7, that when the first nodules developed haemoglobin,

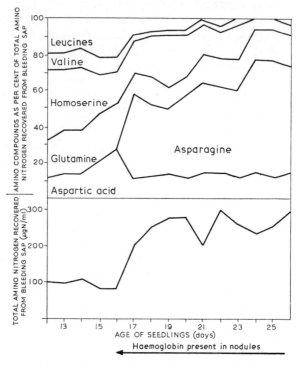

FIG. 7. Abundance of amino compounds found in the bleeding sap of nodulated *Pisum arvense* plants (after ref. 414).

and thus presumably started fixing nitrogen, there was a sudden increase in the exuded amino acids and amides, which were probably liberated from the xylem, and which 3 days after the first appearance of haemoglobin were three times as high as before the pigment appeared. Asparagine comprised the highest proportion (from 50–80 per cent) of the total nitrogen exuded in this species and thus appears to be the main product in which the fixed nitrogen is transferred. Whether this applies to all legumes is as yet unknown, although other workers have recorded high quantities of asparagine in the bleeding sap of nodulated legumes.[567] In the non-legume *Alnus*, citrulline is the most abundant free amino acid in the nodules,[311,344] and much of the nitrogen is transferred from the nodules to the remainder of the plant in this form.[213] Citrulline also occurs in the xylem sap of many non-nitrogen-fixing angiosperms, for example, avocado, birch, hazel, walnut and other woody plants,[67-8,442] so that in plants in general it may play an important rôle in the transfer of nitrogen.

4.4 Physical factors affecting fixation

There are at least three external physical factors which profoundly affect fixation:

1. *Temperature*

It is obvious that temperature will affect the rate of general plant metabolism but, in addition, nitrogen fixation is often specifically inhibited by temperature extremes which do not affect growth. *Trifolium* plants, for example, grow well on combined nitrogen at root temperatures of 20°C and 30°C, but on elemental nitrogen growth is inhibited if the root temperature is increased from 20°C to 30°C.[424] This is not due to an inhibition of nodulation for the number of nodules actually increases at 30°C. It is not due to a specific effect on shoot growth, for increase in shoot temperature from 20°C to 30°C has no effect on fixation. As the nodules are abnormally pigmented at 30°C it is likely that some factor essential for the functioning of the nitrogen-fixing enzyme system within the nodules is affected. Pate, in studies on purple vetch (*Vicia atropurpurea*) and barrel medick (*Medicago tribuloides*), found that nodule numbers were greatest near the extremes of temperature for growth in nitrogen-free medium, and were fewer near the optimum temperature for growth. He suggests that this may be because the nodules which form in the middle of the temperature range are most active in producing substances inhibitory to neighbouring nodule development.[413] In excised roots of *Phaseolus vulgaris*, on the other hand, nodulation is reduced or entirely inhibited by high temperatures which do not affect root growth.[35] In this case it may be due to the inability of the rhizobia to penetrate the roots. No information is available on the nitrogen-fixing ability of the few nodules which do form on *Phaseolus* under these conditions. Thus, in some, but not all instances, high temperature inhibits nodule initiation and development before overall plant growth and when nodules do form their nitrogen-fixing mechanism may be specifically inhibited.

Low temperatures, on the other hand, do not affect the fixation process so markedly. For example, Gukova found that an increase of 4°C above optimum for fixation inhibited fixation by 50 per cent while a decrease of 5°C decreased fixation by only approximately 5 per cent.[234] Furthermore, the effect of low temperatures is not so clear-cut, for although fixation is specifically inhibited in some species,[339-40] for example, soya bean, in others the percentage nitrogen content per plant actually increases, suggesting that processes other than those associated with fixation are first inhibited.[413]

2. *pH*

Studies on the effect of pH on fixation have concentrated, as might be expected with agriculturally important plants such as the legumes, on obtaining optimum conditions for nitrogen fixation, and on determining the range over which it occurs. More attention seems to have been focussed on the effects of low pH on fixation, rather than of high pH, presumably because soils with low pH are more common than those with high values in the temperate regions most extensively studied.

The effect of pH on fixation may be exerted in several ways. In the first instance extremes of pH may affect fixation indirectly by making certain of the inorganic ions unavailable to the plant (for example, molybdenum rapidly becomes unavailable with increasing acidity), while others may become toxic. The legumes, most of which fix nitrogen in the pH range 5–8, are unlikely to be affected by this but it may be important in the case of non-legumes such as *Alnus* and *Myrica* which are characteristic of acid soils. For example Pearsall[416] records *Myrica gale* growing at pH 3·8, although its usual range is 4·3–5·6, and it fixes nitrogen over the pH range 3·3–6·3.[70] Secondly, in many symbiotic systems growth on combined nitrogen occurs at pH extremes which inhibit fixation. For example, red clover grows on ammonium nitrate at pH 4·0, while a pH of 5·0 is necessary for fixation.[539] Similarly the optimum pH for nodulation and fixation in *Myrica gale* is 5·4, although the optimum for growth on combined nitrogen is near to 3·3.[70] On the other hand, if the plants are allowed to nodulate and the pH then lowered to a level which does not permit further nodulation, nitrogen fixation still occurs.[273] This indicates not only that the plants contain an efficient internal pH-regulating mechanism, but also that the nodule organism is more susceptible to low pH than is the host plant, thus explaining the lack of nodulation at low pH levels. Thirdly, fixation may be specifically inhibited, for at the lower pH levels the percentage nitrogen contents of the plants[273] and the nitrogen-fixing efficiency of the nodules[275,277] are reduced.

3. *Light*

The effect of light on fixation has already been discussed in relation to the carbohydrate : nitrogen ratio of the plant. In general, very high light intensities inhibit nitrogen fixation, for example, soya bean plants show symptoms of severe nitrogen deficiency unless combined nitrogen is added. In subterranean clover plants subjected to high light intensity and high temperature only a few large, but ineffective, nodules form.[396]

Light intensity appears to have little effect on rhizobial growth[201] and there is little experimental evidence as far as I am aware, for, or against, the existence of a direct inhibitory effect of light on root infection and nodulation. However as B-indolylacetic acid, which is considered to be a precursor of root-hair infection, may be inactivated by light, exposure of the roots to light could possibly result in a decrease in infection and perhaps also in ultimate nodulation. The period of illumination also affects the degree of nodulation which is generally depressed when short-day plants are placed under long-day conditions and vice-versa.[534]

4.5 Inorganic ions and symbiotic nitrogen fixation

Plants growing on elemental nitrogen require all the major and trace elements necessary for growth on combined nitrogen.

There is evidence that certain of these—molybdenum, iron, and cobalt—are required for symbiotic nitrogen fixation to occur, though whether they are directly involved in the actual nitrogen-fixing mechanism is less certain, as will be seen if we now consider the importance of each of these.

1. *Cobalt*

The necessity of cobalt for the synthesis of the anti-pernicious anaemia vitamin—vitamin B_{12} in animals was well established long before it became obvious that it was necessary for the growth of nodulated plants growing in nitrogen-free medium. Its exact rôle in the latter process is not clear but, as can be seen from Table 3, it is essential for the growth of non-legumes,

TABLE 3. The effect of added cobalt on the growth of nodulated plants and on *Rhizobium*

Species	Nitrogen source	Cobalt supplied (p.p.10^9)	Percentage increase in growth in the presence of cobalt	
Alnus	elemental	0·00	—	ref. 82
glutinosa	nitrogen	10·00	143	
Glycine	elemental	0·00	—	ref. 465
max	nitrogen	0·10	1100	
		1·00	1122	
	ammonium	0·00	—	
	nitrate	0·10	10·1	
		1·00	− 7·2	
Rhizobium	ammonium-	0·00	—	ref. 298
meliloti	nitrogen	0·01	67	
		0·08	74	

legumes, and rhizobia. A requirement for cobalt by non-nodulated legumes growing on combined nitrogen has also been reported recently,[235] although early workers could find none.

In nodulated plants increase in fixation is associated with an increase in the vitamin B_{12} and haemoglobin contents of the nodules. There is also a cobalt requirement for the synthesis of the vitamin B_{12} coenzyme—5,6-dimethylbenzimidazolyl-cobamide, one of several cobamide coenzymes found in nodules[298] and in free-living rhizobia.[299] These findings obviously suggest that the rôle of cobalt in symbiotic nitrogen-fixing plants is multifunctional. In the first instance it may be essential for haemoglobin synthesis. Secondly, free-living rhizobia are rich in vitamin B_{12},[314] and many strains require an exogenous supply of the synthesized vitamin for growth. Thirdly, as mentioned above, it is required for cobamide coenzyme synthesis. Thus, while a direct rôle in fixation cannot be excluded it may well be that the cobalt requirement is simply for healthy growth of the endophytic rhizobia. Although the non-legumes have been less extensively examined, cobamide coenzymes are also present in the nodules,[299] and by analogy it seems probable that the endophytes are also vitamin B_{12}-requirers.

2. Molybdenum

It has been known for many years that molybdenum is essential for the growth of legumes on elemental or combined nitrogen. However as higher concentrations are required when the nitrogen is supplied in the elemental form[256] this suggests an additional requirement for fixation. Early studies on the necessity of molybdenum for fixation provided conflicting results,[254] but it later became clear that this was due to a response being obtained in small-seeded legumes with little seed reserves, for example, clover, but not, or less readily, in large-seeded species, many of which have sufficient seed molybdenum to allow healthy growth through two generations.[254,257,259]

The symptoms of molybdenum deficiency in plants fixing nitrogen are those of nitrogen-deficiency, that is, stunted growth and chlorotic leaves. The nodules are small and scattered over the entire root system, rather than few, large, and aggregated together, as in plants supplied with molybdenum.[40,371] Under conditions of molybdenum deficiency, much of the molybdenum accumulates in the nodules,[274,276,280,370] particularly in the bacteroid tissue.[254]

The rôle of molybdenum in nitrate reduction in plants is well established, but less is known of the part it plays in plants growing in nitrogen-free medium. The degree of nodulation is not specifically inhibited; on the contrary the nodule : plant dry weight ratio actually increases in molybdenum-deficient plants.[258] Nodule efficiency is impaired however and although this could conceivably be due to a shortage of the element for growth of the endophyte, it now seems certain that molybdenum is specifically associated with the nitrogen-fixing enzyme system in free-living nitrogen-fixing micro-organisms (see 7.3), so that it is likely to play a similar part in symbiotic nitrogen fixation. It is of interest to note in this connexion that molybdenum is a component of the catalysts used in chemical nitrogen fixation on a commercial scale.[255]

There is also some evidence that other elements, for example vanadium[41a] and tungsten,[291] can replace molybdenum in nitrogen-fixing organisms, but few data are available for symbiotic plants.

3. *Iron*

Like molybdenum, iron is necessary for healthy growth of symbiotic nitrogen-fixing systems whether they are utilizing elemental or combined nitrogen. There is an additional requirement when the plants are growing solely on elemental nitrogen. Iron obviously plays many rôles in plant metabolism. It is involved in numerous enzyme systems, such as catalases, peroxidases and cytochromes, and those involved in various stages of nitrate reduction, certain of which may also be involved in the fixation of elemental nitrogen if an oxidative pathway is envisaged (see 8.2). An obvious rôle in legume nodules is in relation to haemoglobin synthesis and function. The direct correlation between haemoglobin and nitrogen fixation,[541,551] the evidence from spectral shift studies which shows that in the nodules iron is oxidised in the presence of elemental nitrogen[58,236] and the hypothesis that haemoglobin is associated with, and essential for, nitrogen fixation, all suggest, or depend on, iron being implicated. According to Bergersen[53] almost all the iron present in young (2-day old) soya-bean nodules occurs in the cells in the form of non-haemin iron granules associated with the plastids. These are very similar to the ferritin granules characteristic of mammalian liver where they act as a store for iron released by the degradation of haemoglobin. This is later re-used in the synthesis of further iron compounds.[228,233] It has been suggested that in young nodules these granules provide a reservoir of iron which is used up in the synthesis of haemoglobin and other compounds as the nodules mature and eventually start fixing nitrogen. Similar structures are present however in the plastids of non-nitrogen-fixing plants such as *Zea mays* so that they are probably involved in the metabolism of plastids, rather than specifically associated with symbiotic nitrogen fixation.[137] Ferredoxin (Fd) the non-haem-iron protein involved in fixation in certain free-living nitrogen-fixing organisms (see 7.3) may also be present in root nodules, so that iron may be important in several reactions all concerned with nitrogen fixation.

It should be emphasized that the above data do not provide unequivocal proof that these elements are directly involved in the nitrogen-fixing mechanism, although it seems probable from studies on nitrogen fixation in cell-free extracts of micro-organisms that at least two of them—molybdenum and iron—are. It has also been suggested that other elements such as calcium and copper are directly concerned in the fixation process but the former appears not to be essential in some micro-organisms at least,[168] while insufficient data are available on the latter to allow a definite conclusion to be reached.

4.6 The effect of various gases on nitrogen fixation

Studies on the necessity of various ions for nitrogen fixation were initiated largely to achieve optimum crop yields and maximum levels of fixation. Investigations on the effect of various gases, on the other hand, have been carried out in an attempt to obtain data on the enzyme systems involved in the fixation process. When various partial pressures of a gas are employed the partial pressure is conveniently designated by the letter p preceding the gas in question, for example pN_2 refers to the partial pressure of nitrogen in atmospheres, pO_2 refers to the partial pressure of oxygen etc. It is often more useful to determine or express the results in terms of the Michaelis dissociation constant, that is, to determine the concentration of substrate (in this particular case it will be the partial pressure of gas) at which the reaction rate is half-maximum, and which can be designated by the letters K_m, where m is the substrate in question. For example KN_2 refers to the partial pressure of nitrogen at which the rate of reaction is half-maximum etc. For methods of calculating K_m values in relation to nitrogen fixation, the reader should consult the work of Wilson, Burris and Lind.[587]

1. Nitrogen

The ability of nodulated plants to fix elemental nitrogen efficiently depends on the pN_2 being sufficiently high to saturate the enzyme systems involved. At the nitrogen-fixing centres within the nodule the pN_2 is probably much lower than in the atmosphere outside and it is thus important to determine its effect on fixation. Many experiments have been carried out both on intact plants and on detached nodules, the results indicating that maximum fixation is achieved at a pN_2 near to $0 \cdot 1$ atm. for legumes[579] and $0 \cdot 2$–$0 \cdot 25$ atm. for non-legumes.[76] These values, being much lower than the pN_2 in ordinary air, have practical applications in experiments using ^{15}N, for they show that when using this expensive isotope (approximately £130 per $1 \cdot 0$ gm of elemental nitrogen enriched with 97 atoms per cent ^{15}N), it is possible to reduce the pN_2 of the gas mixture considerably without markedly affecting the fixation rate of the exposed material. The K_{N_2} values are very much lower, for example Burris, Magee and Bach[107] obtained a value of $0 \cdot 025$ atm. for sliced soya bean nodules. The differences in results obtained with various organisms may not be real, however, for the rate of penetration of the gas into the nodule is likely to vary. For example, it would be expected to be much slower in the nodules of non-legumes and in perennial legumes which possess a thick cork-covering than in annual legume nodules. Errors due to this factor would be greater in short-term experiments, for example, in those involving detached nodules. Despite this it is abundantly clear that the pN_2 of normal air ($0 \cdot 8$ atm.) is never likely to limit nitrogen fixation.

2. Hydrogen

The discovery that molecular hydrogen inhibits nitrogen fixation was made unexpectedly by Wilson and his collaborators who, in experiments on the effect of pN_2 on fixation, used hydrogen gas as a presumably inert gas to compensate for low pressures of nitrogen. They discovered that hydrogen was far from inert and that it specifically[591] and competitively[589]

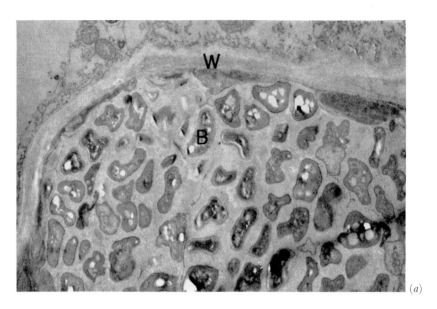

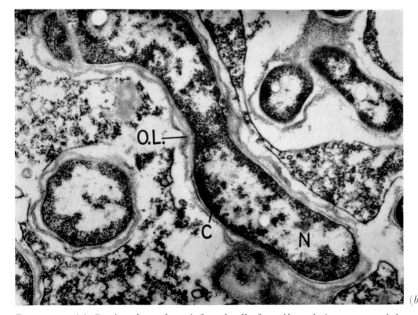

PLATE 5: (*a*) Section through an infected cell of an *Alnus glutinosa* root nodule showing the presence of bacteroid-like cells (B) and host cell wall (W). ×11,000. (*b*) Bacteroid-like cells in *Alnus glutinosa* nodule showing a nucleoid region (N) and cytoplasm (C). Each bacteroid is surrounded by several membranous layers (O.L.). ×25,500.

(a)

(b)

PLATE 6: Nodulated plants of *Alnus glutinosa* (*a*) and *Myrica gale* (*b*), grown for ten weeks in the presence of (from left to right) 0, 10, 50 and 100 mg. per litre of ammonium-nitrogen. $\times \frac{1}{11}$.

inhibited nitrogen fixation. That is, it had no effect if the plants were growing on combined nitrogen, but on gaseous nitrogen it was inhibitory, its effect becoming more pronounced as the pH_2 increased. This suggests that both hydrogen and nitrogen compete for similar enzyme sites and also that a hydrogenase system is involved in fixation. The latter point is supported by the finding that nitrogen-fixing nodules may slowly evolve molecular hydrogen,[54,262] The significance of hydrogenase in nitrogen fixation is referred to later (see 7.4 and 8.7).

3. Oxygen

The effect of various partial pressures of oxygen on fixation is important when one considers that many strict anaerobes, for example *Clostridium*, fix nitrogen, that the formation of ammonia from molecular nitrogen (see 8.3) is a process of reduction, and yet many nitrogen-fixing organisms are obligate aerobes. In the case of symbiotic nitrogen-fixing plants relatively high pO_2 values are required for optimum fixation, being near to that of air (0·2 atm.) for non-legumes[79] and near to 0·5 atm. for legumes (see Fig. 8, p. 56).[51,107] How can such results be reconciled with a reductive nitrogen-fixing pathway? A possible explanation is that although the external pO_2 may be high, the oxygen tension within the nodules may be extremely low.

Evidence that this is the case has been obtained.[16,21,51] For example, Bergersen's data for 32-day-old soya bean nodules (Fig. 8) show that with increase in external pO_2 the nodules exhibit two distinct respiration peaks, the first at 0·5 atm., the other at 0·9–1·0 atm. It has been suggested that the first respiration peak (at 0·5 atm.) is due mainly to respiration by tissue external to the bacteroids and that some 'diffusion barrier' exists between the bacteroids and the exterior. Respiration of the bacteroids does not reach a maximum until the external pO_2 is near 0·9–1·0 atm., which accounts for the second respiration peak. As 2–3 per cent oxygen is the optimum concentration for respiration by bacteroids excised from the nodules, it is evident that in normal air the pO_2 at the nitrogen-fixing sites within the nodules must be very low. Thus fixation is likely to occur under reducing conditions. It is possible that the membrane system which surrounds the bacteroids acts as the barrier.[51]

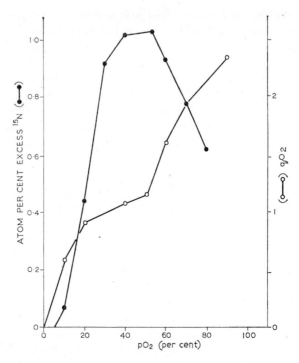

Fig. 8. The relationship between nitrogen-fixation and oxygen tension, and between respiration and oxygen tension, in detached soya bean root nodules (after ref. 51).

4. Carbon monoxide

Carbon monoxide inhibits nitrogen fixation both in legumes[317] and non-legumes,[78] inhibition being specific in that the quantities necessary to inhibit fixation (which may be as low as 0·0001 atm.) do not inhibit uptake of combined nitrogen and have no effect on respiration.[317]

Inhibition is perhaps not unexpected as carbon monoxide is an isostere of molecular nitrogen, that is, it has a similar molecular weight and a similar number of valence electrons. It could thus compete with nitrogen for appropriate enzyme sites on a purely physical basis. This would imply that inhibition should be competitive but this is not the case[317] so that its action

appears physiological. An alternative and not opposed suggestion is that as in mammalian haemoglobin it combines with
nodule haemoglobin to form carboxy-haemoglobin and thus
prevents the efficient functioning of the pigment.

5 Nitrogen Fixation by Free-living Organisms I. Blue-green Algae

5.1

The Myxophyceae, or blue-green algae, are perhaps the most striking nitrogen-fixing organisms yet discovered. They have evolved an advanced self-supporting system, being capable of living photoautrophically in an environment entirely free of combined nitrogen, and yet there is little doubt that they are extremely primitive organisms. They comprise the only class of algae in which nitrogen fixation has been convincingly demonstrated, although claims for fixation by algae from other groups have not been without their advocates. Blue-green algae are of world-wide distribution,[203] being particularly abundant in the moist tropics, where they may aggregate to form gelatinous masses over the soil surface, and contribute appreciably to the nitrogen status of the habitat. Their importance in rice paddyfields doubtless accounts for much of the research carried out on these organisms in far-eastern countries, particularly in India[475] and in Japan.[561] Various aspects of the physiology, biochemistry, and nitrogen-fixing capacity of the blue-green algae have been reviewed by Allen[9,10] and by Fogg.[189−91,193,196]

5.2 Structure

Although these organisms, together with the photosynthetic bacteria, are unique in that the vitally important processes of photosynthesis and nitrogen fixation occur not only within the same organism but within the same cell, their morphological appearance belies their biochemical complexity. In structure they may be unicellular, colonial, or filamentous, but only truly filamentous blue-green algae have so far been found to fix nitrogen. The organisms are characterized as follows:

1. The cell, which is surrounded by a cell wall, and often by a mucilaginous sheath, shows little differentiation, the protoplasm comprising an outer pigmented region—the chromatoplasm, and a central DNA-containing region—the centroplasm. There is no distinct nucleus, large vacuoles, or membrane-bound organelles.

2. The pigments, which are associated with distinct lamellae distributed throughout the chromatoplasm,[122,223,338,408,444,568] are c-phycocyanin (a blue pigment), c-phycoerythrin (a red pigment),[402] chlorophyll a, β-carotene and xanthophylls.[66] These in combination produce the blue-green colour characteristic of the group. The chromatoplasm with photosynthetic lamellae, and the centroplasm, can be clearly distinguished in the electron microscope photograph reproduced in Plate 7a (opposite p. 70).

3. Well defined sexual reproduction is absent, but genetic recombination,[305] and filament anastomosis,[310] occur.

4. The storage product is an amylopectin-like polyglucoside,[268,337] and abundant polyglucoside granules are located in the interlamellar spaces.[223]

General details of the structure of these organisms are available in several reviews.[163a,190,203]

5.3 Nitrogen-fixing species

In tests for nitrogen fixation by large nodulated angiosperms, errors arising from fixation by free-living contaminants are negligible and generally can be ignored, providing suitable controls are included in the experiment. With the Myxophyceae on the other hand, these errors must be eliminated and thus pure cultures are essential. These are difficult to obtain because numerous bacteria harbour in the gelatinous algal sheaths, and in the past, the inability to obtain pure cultures has undoubtedly been a stumbling block in the study of nitrogen fixation by these organisms. At present, pure cultures can be obtained by ultra-violet irradiation (the algae are generally more resistant to ultra-violet light than are the bacteria),[218] by treatment with antibiotics,[421,491] by repeated subculturing on inorganic nitrogen-free medium, or by allowing the algae to grow phototactically through agar leaving the bacteria behind.[97,529] Which of these methods is the most satisfactory depends largely on the species of blue-green algae and bacteria present.

The first tests for fixation by pure cultures (those of Prings-heim's school in 1914[430]) proved negative suggesting that earlier evidence of fixation in impure cultures was due to nitrogen-fixing contaminants. Up till 1928 there was no convincing evidence of fixation, Waksman remarking in 1927, 'it seems to be definitely established that algae are unable to fix atmospheric nitrogen'.[555] In 1928 however, Drewes demonstrated nitrogen fixation by pure cultures of *Anabaena* and *Nostoc* species.[156] Since then at least fourteen genera and about forty species isolated from fresh-water and marine habitats, from hot springs and antarctic wastes and from a host of other environments have been shown to fix nitrogen. There is now no doubt that it is a widespread characteristic in certain families of this group.

Early workers measured fixation by growing the algae in nitrogen-free medium and determined gains in combined nitrogen by Kjeldahl analyses. Fogg[183] stressed the advisability of removing traces of combined nitrogen from the air supplied to such cultures and this modification has subsequently been adopted by many workers. Recently the ^{15}N method has become increasingly popular, and it has been used to demonstrate fixation by intact filaments[106,328,494,572] and by cell-free ex-tracts.[129,462] Providing the culture conditions are suitable these algae can grow as rapidly on molecular nitrogen as they can on combined nitrogen.[12,185,495] The growth rates are relatively slow however compared with certain bacterial nitrogen-fixing species. For example *Nostoc muscorum* one of the fastest grow-ing algal nitrogen fixers to date, has a mean doubling time of about 8 hours[304] which compares with a generation time of under an hour for *Azotobacter*.

It is evident that intact filaments of blue-green algae assimi-late molecular nitrogen under a variety of cultural conditions. However, for optimum fixation they must, in addition to suitable nutrients, have favourable conditions of hydrogen-ion concen-tration, temperature, and light intensity. These factors are dealt with specifically in relation to nitrogen fixation in 7.2, but they are worth considering briefly at this point. Best growth on nitrogen-free medium is achieved under slightly alkaline conditions, for example *Nostoc muscorum* grows best between 7·0 and 8·5 and growth decreases markedly below pH 6·5,[14,558] Others have pH optima near to 9·0.[497] A suitable temperature is of course necessary but these organisms are characterized by being extremely tolerant to temperature changes, for example *Nostoc entophytum*, a brackish-water form fixes nitrogen in the range 5–40°C[497] while *Chlorogloea fritschii* from Indian rice paddy fields has a temperature optimum near to 35–40°C.[176] On the other hand nitrogen-fixing blue-green algae, particularly *Nostoc* species, are abundant in the Antarctic[264–5] and presumably fix nitrogen there. The light intensity for optimal growth depends on various factors such as the density of the culture and the availability of carbon dioxide but, as in symbiotic systems, fixation is impaired if the intensity is too low or too high.[12,195] Unlike many of the nitrogen-fixing bacteria, these algae appear to have no organic growth-factor requirements.[189] Reviews of the effects of various cultural conditions on growth and nitrogen fixation by these organisms are available.[9,189]

The species of blue-green algae now known to fix nitrogen are listed in Table 4 which provides an up-to-date version of that compiled by Fogg and Wolfe in 1954,[193] and Fig. 9 shows the genera in question except *Hapalosiphon*. It is seen that fixation is restricted to the orders Nostocales (except the family Oscillatoriaceae) and the Stigonematales. One nitrogen-fixing alga[176] designated *Chlorogloea fritschii* and once believed to be a member of the Chroococcales[347] has been shown to be a degenerate *Nostoc* species.[177] Recent evidence[160–1] of high fixation rates by impure samples of the genus *Trichodesmium*, a member of the Oscillatoriaceae, is of interest and pure culture studies on this alga are called for. A striking feature of the species shown in pure culture to fix nitrogen is that all contain peculiar cells, which under the light microscope appear to be empty. Such cells are called heterocysts and are absent in non-nitrogen-fixing organisms.

5.4 Heterocysts

These are formed terminally or intercalarily on filaments by ordinary vegetative cells developing a thick wall and appearing

TABLE 4. Nitrogen-fixing blue-green algae

Order and Family	Species which fix nitrogen in pure culture	Reference
NOSTOCALES		
Nostocaceae	*Anabaena ambigua*	474
	A. azollae	536
	A. cycadeae	595
	A. cylindrica	85, 183
	A. fertilissima	474
	A. flos-aquae	227
	A. gelatinosa	141
	A. humicola	85
	A. naviculoides	141
	*A. variabilis**	17, 85, 141, 156
	A. spp.*	156
	Anabaenopsis circularis	559, 560
	Aulosira fertilissima	474
	Chlorogloea fritschii	176
	Cylindrospermum gorakhporense	474
	C. licheniforme	85
	C. maius	85
	C. sphaerica	537
	Nostoc commune	253
	N. calcicola	85
	N. entophytum	491
	N. muscorum	14, 106, 572
	N. paludosum	85
	N. punctiforme	85, 156, 595
	N. spp.	9, 250, 559, 572
	N. sphaericum	407
Rivulariaceae	*Calothrix brevissima*	559, 560
	C. crustacea	11
	C. elenkinii	507
	C. parietina	572
	C. scopulorum	491
Scytonemataceae	*Scytonema hofmanii*	307a
	Tolypothrix tenuis	559, 560
STIGONEMATALES		
Stigonemataceae	*Fischerella muscicola*	307a, 406
	F. major	406
	Hapalosiphon fontinalis	507
	Mastigocladus laminosus	186
	Stigonema dendroideum	535
	Westelliopsis prolifica	415

* A non-nitrogen-fixing strain has been reported.

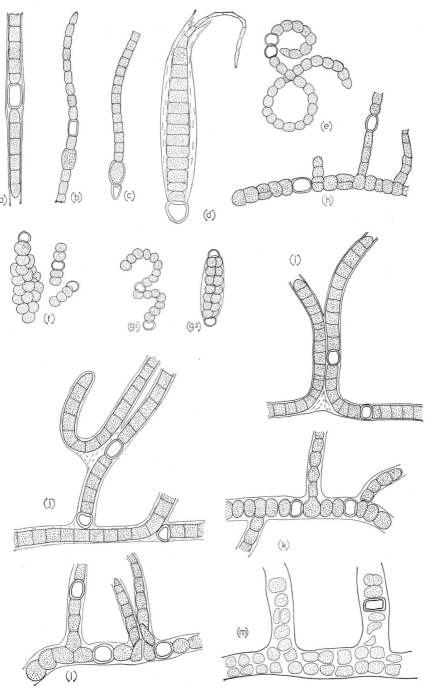

Fig. 9. Nitrogen fixing genera of blue-green algae. The large empty cells are heterocysts. (a) *Aulosira*, (b) *Anabaena*, (c) *Cylindrospermum*, (d) *Calothrix*, (e) *Anabaenopsis*, (f) *Chlorogloea*, (g) *Nostoc*, (h) *Westelliopsis*, (i) *Scytonema*, (j) *Tolypothrix*, (k) *Fischerella*, (l) *Mastigocladus*, (m) *Stigonema*. (× 650 approx.)

to lose their cell contents. In many, but not all species, this is preceded by an increase in size of the cell. Heterocysts are clearly seen in the filaments of *Fischerella* depicted in the frontispiece. Under the electron microscope the mature heterocyst is seen to be connected to the adjacent vegetative cells via a pore in the cell wall, where there is continuity between the cytoplasmic membranes of both cells, but not between the remainder of the protoplasts. As the heterocysts age almost all the cell contents including the photosynthetic lamellae gradually disappear and there is a general absence of granular material except for ribosome-like structures.[569] For detailed information on their development and structure, as seen under the electron microscope and light microscope, the reader is advised to consult the work of Wildon and Mercer,[569] and Fritsch[203-4] and Fogg[187] respectively.

A question that immediately arises in the present context is: are heterocysts in fact the nitrogen-fixing sites—the nodules of the blue-green algae? 'Whole-plant' physiology shows that they react similarly to root nodules in their response to combined nitrogen—they are inhibited by high levels of ammonium-nitrogen, are most abundant in the absence of combined nitrogen, and are stimulated to form by a high carbohydrate : nitrogen ratio in the alga.[184] There are, however, various other aspects in which they react differently to symbiotic nodules and evidence is now accumulating that their relationship to nitrogen fixation is coincidental. This is strongly suggested by the finding that a heterocyst fraction separated from *Anabaena cylindrica* showed no incorporation of ^{15}N when exposed to labelled molecular nitrogen, whereas intact filaments showed high enrichment.[178] Also, as will be seen in 5.5, nitrogen fixation is associated with the photosynthetic lamellae[129] and these are largely absent in mature heterocysts.

Other theories as to their nature and function have been proposed, for example, it has been suggested that they are formed when material is transferred from ordinary vegetative cells to adjacent cells in periods of nitrogen starvation,[187] or that they may be archaic reproductive structures.[215] Several workers have reported germination of heterocysts and according to Wolk this occurs particularly in the presence of ammonium-nitrogen.[602]

5.5 The site of fixation

With the introduction of techniques for preparing active cell-free extracts of blue-green algae,[462] studies on the localization of the nitrogen-fixing sites in these organisms has become possible. Using *Anabaena cylindrica*, Cox and her co-workers obtained cell-free extracts, separated various fractions by centrifugation, exposed these to ^{15}N-labelled molecular nitrogen and measured each for incorporation of the isotope.[129] Highest ^{15}N-enrichment was found in fragments centrifuged down at 35,000g for 20 minutes. This fraction mainly comprised small fragments of intracellular photosynthetic lamellae and it appears certain that fixation is associated with these, particularly as it was also shown that highest photosynthetic activity (as measured by oxygen production) and nitrogen-fixing activity occur in the same fraction. Also, in hydrogen-adapted cells, hydrogenase activity (a characteristic of nitrogen-fixing organisms) is present and is associated with the fractions which contain the pigments chlorophyll and phycocyanin.[205]

5.6 Liberation of extracellular nitrogen

Nitrogen-fixing blue-green algae liberate extracellularly a proportion of the nitrogen fixed during healthy growth.[176,188,492,538] This recalls the excretion of extracellular nitrogen from leguminous roots, and in this instance also, amides, peptides, and free amino acids have been detected.[188] It has been possible to study this process more critically in the blue-green algae than in the legumes because in these algae the exact stage of growth at which excretion is investigated can be easily determined from growth rate data and from microscopic examination. Thus the possibility of measuring extracellular products liberated as a result of cell autolysis can be eliminated. Unlike that of the legumes, the production of extracellular nitrogen in *Anabaena cylindrica*, the organism on which most data are available, does not appear to be governed by variations in the carbohydrate : nitrogen ratio, and a proportion of it is probably not specifically associated with the fixation of nitrogen, for similar extracellular products have been recorded in cultures of non-nitrogen-fixing species.[188,192] The relationship of certain of these extracellular products to nitrogen fixation has been investigated. Using the nitrogen-fixing alga *Westelliopsis prolifica* it has been observed[415] that if the alga was first subjected to a 48-hour period of nitrogen starvation in the light and then exposed to ^{15}N-labelled gaseous nitrogen, ammonia comprised over 50 per cent of the total extracellular nitrogen liberated during the first 30 minutes of fixation, and that the extracellular nitrogen was more highly labelled with ^{15}N than was the cell-nitrogen. On the other hand, if the alga was grown on ^{15}N-labelled gaseous nitrogen for a 48-hour period and then transferred to fresh medium and exposed to normal gaseous nitrogen, amides (probably asparagine and glutamine) were abundant in the medium during the first 30 minutes after exposure. These were more highly labelled with ^{15}N than were the small quantities of extracellular ammonia produced. Thus, the first product of freshly fixed nitrogen liberated into the medium appeared to be ammonia, the extracellular amides were not produced until fixation had proceeded for some time, and were mainly derived from previously fixed nitrogen. This provides additional evidence in favour of ammonia being the key intermediate in nitrogen fixation (see 8.3) a conclusion also arrived at from similar studies on *Clostridium*[611] and *Azotobacter*.[378]

Certain of the extracellular products of blue-green algae influence nitrogen fixation by the organisms which produce them, in that when an algal sample is inoculated into medium in which it has previously been grown for a short time it fixes nitrogen more rapidly than if sub-cultured into a fresh, purely inorganic medium. The extracellular substances responsible for this phenomenon and the mechanism involved are unknown. As mentioned above the extracellular amino acids and peptides do not appear to be specifically associated with the fixation process but they are probably extremely important in natural environments as they provide a mechanism whereby fixed nitrogen can become available to other organisms without cell autolysis being necessary.

5.7 Associations of blue-green algae with other organisms

Although almost all known nitrogen-fixing blue-green algae are capable of healthy growth and nitrogen fixation in the free state, certain species form associations with other organisms. Because the algae fix nitrogen alone, these cannot be regarded as strict nitrogen-fixing symbioses as is the legume-*Rhizobium* association. They range from casual relationships as in the liver-wort *Blasia*, where a *Nostoc* species frequently inhabits cavities on the abaxial surface of the plant, to more distinct associations such as algae and fungi forming specialized lichen thalli, or blue-green algae inducing nodule formation on the roots of the cycads *Encephalartos* and *Ceratozamia*. As there is no degree of uniformity among the associations with various plant groups, it is best to consider each separately.

1. *Associations with fungi*

The association of blue-green algae with fungi to form lichens is probably one of the most striking examples of microbial sym-biosis, for here there results a morphologically distinct end-product quite unlike either of the partners which comprise it.

Studies on nitrogen fixation by intact thalli are few, but using ^{15}N appreciable fixation, which has been attributed to the blue-green algal partners (phycobionts), has been detected in the lichens *Collema granosum*, *Leptogium lichenoides*,[83] and in several species of *Peltigera*,[464,563] but not in *Cladonia impexa*[464] which has a green alga as phycobiont. Direct proof that these blue-green algae fix nitrogen has been provided by the findings that pure cultures of *Nostoc* species isolated from *Peltigera*[563] and *Collema*[250] fix nitrogen. It has been reported that the nitrogen-fixing bac-terium *Azotobacter* is frequently present in lichen thalli,[1] but critical evidence suggests that although this may be so, *Azoto-bacter* is unlikely to contribute appreciably to the total amounts of nitrogen fixed.[83] Like other blue-green algae the phycobionts liberate extracellularly a proportion of the total nitrogen fixed and this may serve as a nitrogen source for the fungal partner (mycobiont).[250-1] There is also evidence from electron micro-scope studies that in the lichenized state certain fungal partners parasitize the alga,[352] so that these may obtain fixed nitrogen directly by the latter method, as well as indirectly in the form of extracellular products. It must be borne in mind, however, that despite the advantages which one would expect a nitrogen-fixing lichen to have on inhospitable substrates low in combined nitrogen, it is a rather inexplicable fact that the majority of lichens contain non-nitrogen-fixing members of the Chlorophyceae, rather than Myxophyceae, as phycobionts, and yet do equally well.

2. Associations with bryophytes and pteridophytes

The occurrence of certain *Nostoc* species within small cavities in the thalli of the bryophytes, *Blasia*[83,348,563] *Cavicularia*,[348,563] and *Anthoceros*,[313] is well known. There seems to be no doubt that the alga in *Blasia*[83,407,563] and *Cavicularia*[563] fixes nitrogen, and in the former probably transfers fixed nitrogen to its hepatic host.[83] The organism in both these liverworts has been identified as *Nostoc sphaericum*[407,563] and although it fixes nitrogen in pure culture, the endophyte of *Anthoceros*, which may not be the same species, apparently does not.[315] Associations with mosses are almost unknown but in Britain a *Hapalosiphon* species occurs on occasion with the bog moss *Sphagnum* where it may become imprisoned within the hyaline cells of the latter. It can also exist freely and preliminary ^{15}N data indicate that the association fixes nitrogen.[497]

Among the pteridophytes the water-fern *Azolla* is the only one with which a blue-green alga (*Anabaena*) is consistently associated. The latter occurs in a ventral pore in the dorsal lobe of each vegetative leaf.[608] Infected plants can grow on nitrogen-free medium,[455] the isolated endophyte fixes nitrogen,[537] and liberates extracellularly amino acids which may provide a nitrogen source for the pteridophyte.[538]

3. Associations with gymnosperms and angiosperms

Many genera of the family Cycadaceae, for example *Cycas*, *Encephalartos*, *Stangeria*, *Ceratozamia*, *Macrozamia* and *Zamia* bear on their roots characteristic coralloid masses which are superficially rather similar to the nodules of non-leguminous angiosperms such as *Alnus*. Unlike the latter, the endophyte, which forms a distinct zone in air spaces in the cortex (see Fig. 10), is a blue-green alga, variously referred to as an *Anabaena* or *Nostoc*. It has been established on the basis of growth in nitrogen-free medium that the endophytes of *Cycas*,[155,595] *Stangeria*,[155] and *Encephalartos*,[595] fix nitrogen and this has been confirmed using

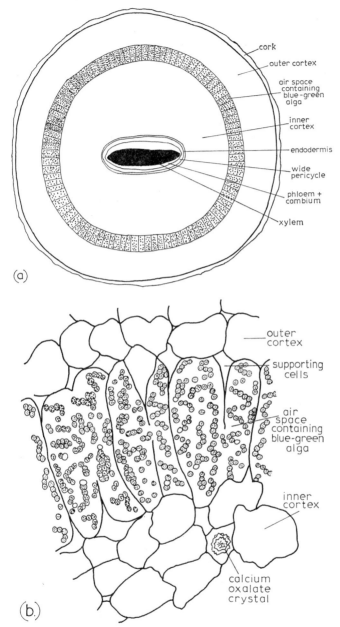

(a)

(b.)

FIG. 10. Transverse section through a root nodule of *Encephalartos* sp. as seen under (a) low power × 20, and (b) high power × 150 of the microscope.

[15]N for the endophytes of *Cycas* and *Encephalartos*, and for *Macrozamia*.[563] The latter method has also established fixation by the nodules of *Ceratozamia*, *Encephalartos*,[77] and *Cycas*.[563] Earlier reports of the presence of nitrogen-fixing bacteria within the nodules of certain cycads[316,334,461,483] have been attributed to surface contamination.[458]

The association of a *Nostoc* species with *Gunnera*, a large perennial angiosperm belonging to the family Haloragidaceae, and characteristic of moist habitats, particularly in the southern hemisphere, has long been known. The alga, which occurs intra-cellularly within wart-like swellings on the leaf bases, has been isolated, said to fix nitrogen,[240] and identified as *Nostoc puncti-forme*.[595] The latter species has also been recorded within root nodules of the legume *Trifolium alexandrinum*.[63] Although this would appear to be a casual relationship, much greater nitrogen fixation by the blue-green alga occurs in mixed cultures of *Nostoc calcicola* and *Rhizobium* strains than in *Nostoc* cultures alone, the rhizobia becoming bacteroid-like in the mixed cul-tures.[62] It seems likely however that the better growth of *Nostoc* in the latter is simply a result of increased availability of carbon dioxide as a result of bacterial respiration.

4. *Other associations*

In addition to the above relatively well-known associations, there are others which have received little attention. Such is the association of *Nostoc entophytum*, a known nitrogen-fixing blue-green alga which has been recorded intracellularly in certain other marine algal species,[491] or that of the known nitrogen-fixing genus *Calothrix*[572,491] within the thallus of the green alga *Enteromorpha*.[308] Perhaps the most curious finding of all is that of a heterocystous (and thus probably nitrogen-fixing) species within the cells of certain marine rhizosolenias sp. (diatoms).[203] In the latter two cases fixation by the blue-green algal species in question has still to be demonstrated.

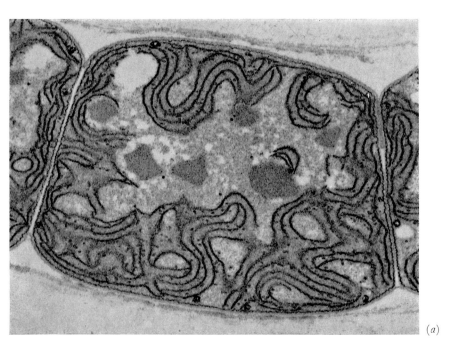

(a)

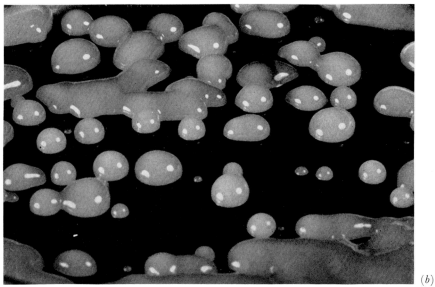

(b)

PLATE 7: (a) L.S. through a vegetative cell of the nitrogen-fixing blue-green alga *Nostoc muscorum* showing outer chromatoplasm and inner centroplasm. ×31,000. (b) Colonies of the nitrogen-fixing bacterium *Beijerinckia*. ×1⅓.

6 Nitrogen Fixation by Free-living Organisms II. Bacteria

6.1

The first experimental evidence that micro-organisms fixed elemental nitrogen was apparently presented in 1862 by the French scientist Jodin who, by measuring the disappearance of gaseous nitrogen from a closed system in which 'végétaux mycodermiques' and 'les mucédinées' were growing, concluded that they fixed the nitrogen.[285] It is probable that certain of these organisms were bacteria. In 1885 Berthelot,[60] continuing along similar lines, showed that unsterilized soils fixed nitrogen, whereas sterilized soils did not, but it was a further eight years before a bacterium capable of fixing molecular nitrogen was isolated in pure culture. This organism, isolated by Winogradsky in 1893[597] from soil by repeated subculturing, was the anaerobic spore-former *Clostridium pastorianum* (now *C. pasteurianum*). In 1901 Beijerinck discovered that the aerobes *Azotobacter chroococcum* and *A. agilis* did likewise.[46] For almost fifty years thereafter studies centred round the physiology of these two genera. In 1949 however Kamen and Gest obtained evidence that the photosynthetic bacterium *Rhodospirillum rubrum* fixed nitrogen.[290] This discovery was prompted by the finding that just as nitrogen fixation in general is inhibited by molecular hydrogen, hydrogenase activity in photosynthetic bacteria is inhibited by gaseous nitrogen or ammonia. Thus, it seemed likely that photosynthetic bacteria such as *R. rubrum* should fix nitrogen, and critical work using ^{15}N amply confirmed this in several photosynthetic bacteria.[318-21] It is now obvious that the ability to fix nitrogen is not of such restricted occurrence among bacteria as was once thought, for it seems possible that under certain conditions a wide range of species fix nitrogen. To date, evidence for fixation by at least eighteen bacterial genera of diverse physiological ability and from widely differing habitats is available. These are listed in Table 5 and

TABLE 5. Genera of bacteria with known nitrogen-fixing species
(see text for references)

Order and Family	Genus	mg nitrogen fixed per gm carbohydrate utilized
EUBACTERIALES		
Achromobacteraceae	*Achromobacter*	1
Azotobacteraceae	*Azotobacter*	10–20
	Beijerinckia	10–20
	Derxia	< 25
Bacillaceae	*Bacillus*	12
	Clostridium	2–27
Enterobacteriaceae	*Aerobacter*	4–5
	Klebsiella	5
PSEUDOMONADALES		
Athiorhodaceae	*Rhodospirillum*	–
	Rhodopseudomonas	–
	Rhodomicrobium	–
Thiorhodaceae	*Chromatium*	–
Chlorobacteriaceae	*Chlorobium*	–
Pseudomonadaceae	*Azotomonas*	
	Pseudomonas	1–4
Spirillaceae	*Desulfovibrio*	–
	Methanobacterium	–
	Spirillum or *Vibrio*	–

the chief characteristics of each group will be briefly considered below.

6.2 The Azotobacteraceae

This family of gram-negative, strictly aerobic, heterotrophic rods, comprises the nitrogen-fixing genera *Azotobacter*, *Beijerinckia* and *Derxia*. *Azotomonas*, once considered to be a member of the Azotobacteraceae is now placed in the Pseudomonadaceae.[90] *Azotobacter*, the commonest genus, is of world-wide occurrence in soil and water, except in polar regions where it is rare. The organisms are highly pleomorphic being 4–6×2–3 μ in size and it is now generally considered that there are three species, *A. chroococcum*, *A. agilis* and *A. vinelandii* although in the 1957 edition of Bergey's *Manual of Determinative Bacteriology* the latter is not recognized as a distinct species.[90] Of these three organisms, *A. vinelandii* has been studied most extensively and has been used, particularly by Nicholas and his co-workers, as a source of nitrogen-fixing cell-free extracts.[380,381] It fixes nitrogen best under slightly alkaline conditions, fixation is rapidly inhibited below pH 6,[102] and the optimum temperature for fixation and growth is near 25–28 °C. Although strictly aerobic, fixation by *Azotobacter* may be specifically inhibited at high pO_2 levels.[410] It is probably the most rapidly growing nitrogen-fixing bacterium known, but its efficiency in fixation is not greater than that of certain other nitrogen-fixing organisms, being of the order of 10–20 mg nitrogen fixed per 1·0 gm sugar consumed.

The genus *Beijerinckia* was created in 1950 when it was decided[144] that an organism initially isolated from Indian rice fields as *Azotobacter indicum*,[487] differed so markedly in its morphological and physiological characters (it produces abundant mucilage as can be seen in Plate 7*b*, and fixes nitrogen vigorously under acid conditions) that it should be placed in a separate genus as *B. indica*.[144] Other species have since been described. The genus is typical of, and widely distributed in, tropical and lateritic soils and has been studied in detail, particularly by Becking.[39,41,41a] Because of its morphological and cultural resemblances to rhizobia, it has been suggested that it may be the ancestral type of *Rhizobium* which has retained its nitrogen-fixing ability in the free state,[145] but in the words of Jensen[279] this possibility 'remains a fascinating hypothesis—nothing more'. It is a characteristic genus of the 'phyllosphere', that is the leaf surface, of plants of tropical rain forests, for example in Indonesia, Java and Sumatra, and it has been suggested that the higher plant may benefit from uptake by the leaves of the nitrogen fixed, while exudation from the leaves supplies the necessary organic and mineral nutrients for the micro-organisms.[450-1] Much more research has still to be undertaken both on the abundance of *Beijerinckia* and other nitrogen-fixing organisms in this ecological niche, and on the amounts of nitrogen fixed, but if the association is of widespread and abundant occurrence, its contribution to the overall nitrogen status of tropical forests may be considerable.

The genus *Derxia* comprises one species *D. gummosa*. This organism, which has only recently been discovered and assigned to the Azotobacteraceae, is a gram-negative, aerobic rod, 3–6 × 1·0–1·2 μ in size, which has been isolated from West Bengal soils.[282] It is a very efficient nitrogen-fixing organism, up to 25 mg nitrogen being fixed per gram of glucose consumed. This is a more efficient conversion rate than that achieved by any other member of the Azotobacteraceae. Fixation occurs in the pH range 5·0–9·0, and in the temperature range 15–42 °C with an optimum between 25 °C and 35 °C.

6.3 The photosynthetic bacteria

In these pigmented bacteria the photosynthetic pigments, as seen under the electron microscope, are aggregated in lamellae rather similar to those of the blue-green algae or in membrane-bound vesicles or chromatophores.[221] Like symbiotic nitrogen-fixing plants and the Myxophyceae they utilize carbon dioxide as a carbon source and derive their energy directly from sunlight, but unlike these they require, in addition to water exogenous reductants such as molecular hydrogen, hydrogen sulphide, certain fatty acids, and alcohols.

There are three groups of photosynthetic bacteria, separated on the basis of their pigmentation and biochemistry: the Chlorobacteriaceae, the Thiorhodaceae, and the Athiorhodaceae. The chief characteristics of each group are summarized in Table 6 but the differences between the species of different groups are not always clear cut. The Chlorobacteriaceae and Thiorhodaceae frequently occur in Nature in environments rich in hydrogen sulphide and exposed to light. The Athiorhodaceae are typical of stagnant water and soil. For general details of these organisms the reviews by van Niel and others should be consulted.[163a,221,312,484–5,531–3]

Among the Chlorobacteriaceae, *Chlorobium*, a small non-motile, gram-negative, rod or oval-shaped form, generally 0·8 × 0·9–1·5 μ in size, is the only genus so far shown to fix gaseous nitrogen. It is a strict anaerobe. Fixation occurs in the light on purely mineral media at pH 7 and in experiments using ^{15}N-labelled molecular nitrogen enrichments of 0·318 and 0·203 atom per cent excess ^{15}N have been demonstrated,[321] so that there is no doubt that the genus fixes nitrogen. In *Chromatium*, a motile, oval or kidney-shaped form, belonging to the Thiorhodaceae fixation by whole cells is largely light dependent and fixation can be stimulated by the addition of pyruvate.[47] Cell-free extracts fix nitrogen in the dark, but activity is low, even when stimulated by the addition of reduced diphosphopyridine nucleotide (NADH$_2$) or molecular hydrogen.[25] Several genera

TABLE 6. General characteristics of photosynthetic bacteria (after ref. 603)

Family	Habitat	Exogenous reductants*	Hetero-trophic growth*	Growth factor require-ments
Chloro-bacteriaceae	Mainly sulphide containing	Sulphide (*more oxidized forms of inorganic* S)	None	None
Thiorhodaceae	Mainly sulphide containing	Inorganic S compounds, hydrogen, organic acids	None	None
Athior-hodaceae	Mainly containing organic compounds	Organic compounds (*Inorganic* S *compounds, hydrogen*)	(*Aerobic only, on substrates used in light*)	One or more vitamin B-group substances

* Properties listed in (*italics*) are shown only by some organisms in the family.

belonging to the Athiorhodaceae: *Rhodospirillum*, *Rhodopseudomonas* and *Rhodomicrobium* fix nitrogen, and of the various species *Rhodospirillum rubrum*, a spiral-shaped form, $1-4 \times 1 \cdot 5-7 \mu$ in size, has been the most extensively studied. This organism fixes nitrogen anaerobically in the light and intact cells stop fixing nitrogen immediately they are placed in the dark,[427] but in cell-free extracts fixation may be of the same order in the light and in the dark.[462]

6.4 Clostridium

Clostridium, the first bacterial genus shown to fix nitrogen in pure culture, comprises a group of strictly anaerobic, spore-forming, gram-positive rods. Although widespread in distribution the organisms are seldom very abundant. The optimum temperature for fixation is near to 25 °C, and the majority of the species tested apparently fix nitrogen, although *C. pasteurianum* is the only one which has been extensively studied in this connexion. Its nitrogen-fixing efficiency is generally low, being of the order of 2–3 mg nitrogen fixed per 1·0 gm of carbohydrate consumed, although a nitrogen-fixing efficiency as high as 27 mg nitrogen per 1·0 gm of carbohydrate has been recorded for *C. butyricum*.[409] Studies on cell-free extracts of *C. pasteurianum* have probably contributed more to our understanding of the nitrogen-fixing enzyme systems in plants than have investigations on any other single organism, as will be seen later (8.7).

6.5 Other nitrogen-fixing bacteria

The relatively widespread ability of organisms other than the above to fix nitrogen is shown, for example, by the experiments of Proctor and Wilson who demonstrated that six *Pseudomonas* strains and eight *Achromobacter* strains isolated under non-selective conditions assimilated ^{15}N-labelled gaseous nitrogen.[431] The nitrogen-fixing capacity of the genus *Pseudomonas*, a group of small, motile, flagellated, gram-negative rods, was first demonstrated in 1955.[20,554] Fixation may occur under aerobic, or anaerobic (except in *P. azotogensis*) conditions, and as in most other nitrogen-fixing organisms a hydrogenase system is present. The nitrogenase in certain strains at least is adaptive, in that on transferring the organism from ammonium-nitrogen to molecular nitrogen, no fixation occurs for several hours,[432] but this lag phase may be reduced by the addition of biotin.[433] Recently a methane-oxidizing *Pseudomonas* capable of fixing nitrogen has also been isolated.[139] Another organism closely related to *Pseudomonas* is *Azotomonas*. It is reported to fix nitrogen[486] but it has not been extensively studied in this connexion. All strains of *Achromobacter* tested by Proctor and Wilson were aerobic but one[284] also fixed nitrogen anaerobically. Because of the widespread occurrence of *Pseudomonas* and *Achromobacter* in soils and water, they may be important nitrogen-fixing organisms in Nature and the former genus occurs along with *Beijerinckia* in the phyllosphere populations of certain tropical rain forests.[451]

Another nitrogen-fixing gram-negative rod is the genus *Aerobacter*. This bacterium was first reported to fix nitrogen in 1928,[477] but this was not confirmed till almost twenty-five years later.[237] The organisms, which contain an adaptive nitrogenase, have an optimum temperature of 15–18 °C for nitrogen fixation, grow best at pH 6–8, but not below 3·5–3·6.[283] The effect of pO_2 on fixation varies with the strain, for example Jensen[283] observed equal fixation under aerobic and anaerobic conditions, while Hamilton and Wilson[237] found that molecular oxygen specifically inhibited the process. Gaseous hydrogen inhibits nitrogen fixation under anaerobic conditions and *Aerobacter* was the first organism in which this was demonstrated.[418]

There is evidence that certain species of the genus *Bacillus* fix nitrogen. In 1908 fixation was recorded in *B. asterosporus*[89] which is now considered to be similar to *B. polymyxa*, a species in which fixation has been demonstrated using [15]N.[230] Fifteen out of seventeen *B. polymyxa* strains tested fix nitrogen, and grow over the temperature range 25–37 °C, but not at 43 °C. All require anaerobic conditions for fixation, as little as one per cent oxygen completely inhibiting fixation, although they grow aerobically or anaerobically on ammonium-nitrogen. As in *Aerobacter*, high partial pressures of molecular hydrogen inhibit fixation, which in cell-free extracts is stimulated by the addition of pyruvate.[229] Other nitrogen-fixing strains of *Bacillus* have been isolated from African soils[350] but only two have been studied in any detail.[351] One appears to have a hydrogenase system. Like *B. polymyxa* there is a growth factor requirement for fixation, although this is not biotin as in the latter species.

Other bacteria reported to fix nitrogen are a *Vibrio* or *Spirillum* species,[43] *Methanobacterium*,[420] *Desulfovibrio*[476] and an unidentified species from jute soil[449] but few detailed studies on nitrogen fixation by these organisms have been carried out. It has been suggested that *Desulfovibrio* may not in fact fix atmospheric nitrogen and that the earlier positive evidence is erroneous.[31]

6.6 Nitrogen fixation in bacterial cell-free extracts

The advantages of using cell-free extracts to study biological nitrogen fixation have long been realized, but early reports that cell-free preparations had been achieved, for example from

Azotobacter[30] were not substantiated. In the 1950's fixation by cell-free extracts was reported, but the results were not reproducible.[263,329] At least these early successes encouraged the hope that the ultimate preparation of reliable nitrogen-fixing extracts was not very far off. It also became possible to obtain nitrogen-fixing bacterial 'protoplasts' by dissolving away the cell-wall with lysozyme. Such protoplasts fixed nitrogen efficiently, but not as well as did intact cells.[289] This may have been due to inhibitory effects of the medium rather than to a loss of substances associated with fixation. That nitrogen-fixing cell-free extracts could be prepared consistently became evident in 1960 (for references see p. 6) and since these were first obtained with bacteria it is appropriate to consider briefly at this point the common methods of preparing them. One is to subject the cells to an extremely high pressure so that cell-disruption occurs. This is generally done in one of the two following types of press —the Hughes press[269] or the French press.[345] In the former, the cell suspension is frozen and disruption is effected by the grinding of the ice crystals. In the latter disruption is thought to occur as the cells are forced through a narrow aperture under pressure. After disruption of the cells, the various fractions are obtained by centrifugation. A second method is to use a combination of vacuum drying and cell autolysis. This involves drying the cells rapidly *in vacuo* and then resuspending them in a suitable buffer solution for a period, during which time the nitrogen-fixing enzymes are obtained in solution and may subsequently be separated from the cell debris by centrifugation. Using this method it is possible to extract large quantities of the nitrogen-fixing enzyme systems at once, and it has frequently been used in work on *Clostridium*.[117-8] The third method commonly used, either alone,[238,462] or in combination with the enzyme lysozyme[381] which aids disruption of the cell wall, is to disintegrate the cells by ultrasonic vibration. As with the other methods, the various fractions are obtained by centrifugation.

Cell-free extracts are now routinely used in several laboratories in the study of bacterial nitrogen fixation. Few additions, if any, are necessary for fixation to occur in the extracts and these differ according to the organism in question, as can be seen from Table 7 in which the organisms from which cell-free

TABLE 7. Additives which support nitrogen fixation by cell-free extracts of various micro-organisms

Organism	Additives	References
Azotobacter vinelandii	Factor present in aged medium + 10 per cent oxygen	381, 382
	or Clostridium hydrogenase + ATP + ferredoxin	95
	or ATP + sodium dithionite ($Na_2S_2O_4$)	96
Bacillus polymyxa	Pyruvate	229
Clostridium pasteurianum	Pyruvate (α-ketobutyrate partially substitutes)	117,118
	or ATP + ferredoxin + H_2	358
Chromatium sp.	None required (H_2 or $NADH_2$ stimulate)	25
Rhodospirillum rubrum	Pyruvate	112
	or ATP + sodium dithionite	96
	(α-ketoglutarate stimulates)	112
Anabaena cylindrica	None required (pyruvate stimulates)	462 130
Calothrix parietina	None required	462
Chlorogloea fritschii	None required (pyruvate stimulates)	175
Mastigocladus laminosus	None required	462
Nostoc muscorum	None required	462

extracts have been obtained, and their requirements for fixation are listed. For completeness the data on blue-green algae are also included. The requirements are mainly simple reducing compounds, or possible sources of reducing power and energy. Presumably in extracts which fix nitrogen without any addition, a plentiful supply of these substances, or substances of similar function, are available in the nitrogen-fixing fraction. In bacterial extracts, the highest nitrogen-fixing activity is generally found in the water-soluble supernatant fraction even after prolonged centrifugal treatment. For example, in *Clostridium pasteurianum* maximum activity is still in the supernatant after centrifugation at 144,000 *g* for 4 hours.[362] In *Azotobacter* highest activity is found in the pellet fraction, and in this respect resembles the blue-green algae.[129] It also contains a particulate fraction with nitrogen-fixing activity which remains in the supernatant, except after very prolonged centrifugation, but the nature of this, or of the various pellet fractions has apparently not been investigated. However in *Achromobacter* maximum activity is found in a wall and membrane fraction[238] as in blue-green algae. Organisms in which maximum nitrogen-fixing activity is associated with a supernatant water-soluble fraction are obviously the most suitable for studies on the enzymic mechanisms involved, as the use of a soluble enzyme system eliminates many of the other metabolic effects which may be associated with a particulate fraction. At the same time no clues are provided as to the actual site of fixation.

6.7 Liberation of nitrogenous extracellular products

Like the blue-green algae, nitrogen-fixing bacteria liberate fixed nitrogen into the medium during healthy growth. This phenomenon has been studied in *Clostridium*[611] and *Azotobacter*,[378] and it has been found that during short exposure periods to ^{15}N-labelled gaseous nitrogen, extracellular ammonia and amides (asparagine and glutamine) predominate in the medium. The ammonia, followed by the amides, is most highly labelled, while the cells show little enrichment. As already mentioned in relation to the blue-green algae, this discovery has been one of the chief points supporting the theory that ammonia is the key intermediate in biological nitrogen fixation.[584] These and other extracellular products may be important in the overall fixation process, as evidenced by the finding that under certain conditions a substance, or substances, present in aged *Azotobacter vinelandii* medium are necessary before cell-free extracts of this organism fix nitrogen.[380] It may of course be that in *Azotobacter* the extracellular products may not be directly involved in fixation. They may act as chelating agents, as do the extracellular products of blue-green algae.[194]

6.8 Associations of nitrogen-fixing bacteria with other organisms

There are numerous reports in the literature of nitrogen-fixing associations between bacteria and other organisms which range from microscopic algae such as *Volvox*,[441] to certain insects.[521-3]

Because of the lack of critical or confirmatory data, or both, all such claims can apparently be rejected, but it is possible that some associations may yet be found.

In the plant kingdom associations of nitrogen-fixing bacteria with higher plants have been reported. These are the leaf gland and leaf nodule associations.

Leaf glands, which contain bacteria embedded in mucilage, occur terminally on the leaves of *Dioscorea macroura*, a member of the tropical monocotyledenous family Dioscoreaceae. The bacteria, which are flagellated gram-positive rods $1\cdot6$–$2\cdot4 \times 0\cdot6$–$0\cdot8$ μ in size, are said to fix nitrogen in pure culture, and the glandular region has a higher percentage nitrogen content than the remainder of the leaf.[405] Stipular glands inhabited by bacteria are also present on species of *Coprosma*, a genus of the family Rubiaceae, and assimilation of ^{15}N-labelled molecular nitrogen by the shoots of this genus has been demonstrated,[489] although the causative organism has not yet been isolated.

More is known about the leaf nodules, first reported in higher plants in 1902 by Zimmermann,[612] and found in members of the families Rubiaceae and Myrsinaceae. In the former family there are three genera which have been reported to bear nitrogen-fixing nodules. These are *Psychotria*, *Pavetta* and *Chomelia*. Reliable evidence of fixation has been obtained for *Psychotria* by Silver and his co-workers using modern methods,[471] thus confirming early reports of fixation. *Psychotria* is a shrubby plant up to six feet tall. The leaf nodules are, in effect, subepidermal cavities filled with slime and bacteria, and each is associated with a vascular bundle. Several hundred nodules may be scattered over the leaf surface or arranged linearly along the mid-rib. Homogenates of the leaves of some plants fix small but significant quantities of ^{15}N-labelled gaseous nitrogen and the isolated endophyte, a gram-negative, motile, non-sporing species of the genus *Klebsiella*, fixes considerable quantities of nitrogen in the free state, indicating that the association is not necessary for fixation to occur.[471] Nodulated plants can grow normally in nitrogen-free medium, but even in the presence of combined nitrogen growth of non-nodulated plants is abnormal.[270] It was suggested by some early workers that this is because the bacteria supply an essential growth factor, a suggestion supported by the finding that gibberellic acid partially replaces the bacteria in allowing normal growth on combined nitrogen.[471] There is evidence that the scattered leaf nodules of the tropical shrub *Pavetta* also contain a nitrogen-fixing endophyte. According to von Faber[169-70] the endophyte is identical with that in *Psychotria* and was named *Mycobacterium rubiacearum*, but recent work by Centifanto and Silver suggests that von Faber may have mis-identified the organism and that its characteristics are very similar to those of the *Klebsiella* species which they isolated from *Psychotria*.[120] According to Rao the leaf nodules on *Chomelia asiatica* contain nitrogen-fixing gram-positive rods.[440] In the family Myrsinaceae, leaf nodules occur on *Ardisia*, a genus of approximately 240 species from tropical America, Asia and Australia. Evidence for,[239] and against,[343,373] the ability of the nodule bacteria to fix nitrogen has appeared in the literature. In what appears to be the most recent publication, the bacterium from *Ardisia hortorum* nodules has been identified as a species of *Xanthomonas*. It is said to fix nitrogen and to supply an essential growth factor to the plant.[239]

It is clear that even although nitrogen fixation by the leaf nodule bacteria of *Psychotria* has been unequivocally demonstrated the position regarding the others is not at all satisfactory. Also, since the results of Ruinen[450,451] on the abundance of nitrogen-fixing bacteria in the phyllosphere the picture has become even more complicated. It is obvious that a great deal of work on nitrogen fixation by leaf nodule associations has still to be carried out and a good starting point for such work would be a re-examination of the earlier claims for fixation.

6.9 Nitrogen fixation by other free-living micro-organisms

In the Introduction it was mentioned that micro-organisms other than the blue-green algae and bacteria may fix elemental nitrogen and these organisms, which are almost all fungi, may now be briefly considered. Among the larger fungi there are reports of fixation by the basidiomycete genus *Phoma*,[286,511] but these have not been confirmed using the critical ^{15}N method.[582] More recently evidence has been presented for fixation by certain soil yeasts, for example it has been shown, both by conventional Kjeldahl analyses and by the ^{15}N method, that two yeasts, a *Rhodotorula* and *Saccharomyces*, isolated from a *Betula-Calluna* heath, fixed nitrogen.[342] The efficiency of the organisms in fixation is of the order of 1–4 mg nitrogen fixed per gram of carbohydrate consumed. In addition, twenty other nitrogen-fixing strains of yeast were isolated from soil.[342] A marine *Rhodotorula* may also fix nitrogen but little is known of its physiology.[11] Another organism said to fix nitrogen is a *Pullularia*-type yeast which fixes 4–5 mg nitrogen per gram of carbohydrate consumed.[92] Two yeasts (probably *Saccharomyces* species) isolated from the root nodules of lupin in Hungary apparently fix nitrogen, the plants containing the yeasts growing better than those in which they are absent. These organisms, which have an optimum temperature of 25 °C, fix nitrogen below pH 3 and have an efficiency of 2·4–5·7 mg nitrogen fixed per gram carbohydrate utilized.[374–5] They contain a red pigment, the abundance of which is directly correlated to the nitrogen-fixing efficiency of the organisms and this was first thought to be haemoglobin, but now appears not to be.[376] It should be noted that nitrogen fixation is not a characteristic of all yeasts, for Lindstrom, Lewis and Pinsky[319] using ^{15}N could not detect fixation in bakers' yeast. Although haemoglobin has been found in certain fungi, for example *Penicillium* and *Neurospora*,[293–4] there is no correlation between the presence of haemoglobin in a fungus and a nitrogen-fixing capacity. The report[341] that two species of the actinomycete genus *Nocardia* fix nitrogen is of special interest as it is now generally accepted that the endophytes of the nitrogen-fixing non-legumes are also actinomycetes (see 3.4). The reported nitrogen-fixing efficiency of *Nocardia cellulans* is high, as much as 12 mg nitrogen being fixed per 1·0 gm of carbohydrate (cellulose) utilized.

In conclusion it is important to note that the evidence for fixation by fungi and actinomycetes has been obtained almost entirely by the Kjeldahl method. As mentioned previously this method is less satisfactory with micro-organisms than that using the ^{15}N technique. Much more positive evidence for fixation by these organisms using the ^{15}N method has still to be obtained before the evidence is as strong as that available for fixation by certain Eubacteriales, Pseudomonadales and blue-green algae.

7 Nitrogen Fixation by Free-living Organisms III. Physiology

7.1

Studies on the physiology of nitrogen fixation by free-living organisms are in certain respects simpler than those on symbiotic systems, in that the material is much more easily handled in the laboratory, it grows more quickly, it can be obtained in pure culture relatively easily, and there are no root nodules to complicate the picture. Apart from such differences, the physiology of the two groups is very similar, and in general, studies on one have complemented findings on the other. However, it has often been possible, as will be seen below, to gain additional information from the studies on microbial cultures, for in these, all, or almost all, the cells fix nitrogen so that the effects of various treatments are often expressed much quicker than in symbiotic systems with a high proportion of non-nitrogen-fixing tissue.

7.2 The effect of various physical factors on fixation

As in symbiotic systems the most important of these appear to be temperature, pH, and light intensity.

1. *Temperature*

The optimum temperature for fixation varies widely in different organisms and is often related to the temperature of the habitat from which the particular micro-organism has been isolated. For example, certain *Azotobacter* strains from tropical soils have temperature optima up to 40 °C,[41] while the optimum temperatures for *Westelliopsis prolifica*, a blue-green alga from Indian rice fields, and for certain marine species of blue-green algae from temperate shores, are near to 35 °C[415] and 25 °C respectively.[497] It seems to be a general rule that fixation is inhibited to a greater extent by extremes of temperature than are other physiological processes such as respiration and photosynthesis. For example from the results of Fogg and Than-Tun for *Anabaena cylindrica* reproduced in Figs. 11 and 12 it is obvious that photosynthesis occurs at extremes of temperature which inhibit fixation.[195] These data also indicate that increases in temperature above the optimum affect fixation to a greater extent than do comparable decreases in temperature. Such results agree closely with those obtained for symbiotic nitrogen-fixing plants.

2. *Hydrogen ion concentration*

Just as nitrogen-fixing micro-organisms grow and assimilate gaseous nitrogen at very varying temperatures, so also do they grow and fix nitrogen at very different hydrogen-ion concentrations, for example *Nostoc muscorum* fixes nitrogen at pH 9·0,[14] while certain *Beijerinckia* strains will do so at pH 3·0.[41] Generally speaking, blue-green algae fix nitrogen optimally under slightly alkaline conditions while bacteria do so at a pH near to neutrality. Exceptions such as *Beijerinckia* do of course occur. At a low pH fixation in bacteria may be specifically inhibited, for example *Azotobacter* cannot fix nitrogen below pH 6·0, although it will grow on combined nitrogen at pH 5·0.[102] At high pH levels the opposite appears to be the case, for here respiration is inhibited before nitrogen fixation. In blue-green algae, on the other hand, no differential effect of hydrogen-ion concentration on growth and fixation has been established. The ability of these organisms to grow at such varying pH levels does not imply that the internal pH of the organisms also varies to the same extent—indeed the enzyme systems could not function at the extremes of pH at which certain organisms fix nitrogen. They must possess therefore an efficient internal pH-regulating mechanism. That this is so is exemplified by studies on nitrogen fixation by *Clostridium pasteurianum*. In cell-free extracts of this organism the optimum pH for fixation is 6·3–6·6, fixation falling off markedly outside these limits, for example samples kept at pH 6 for 8 hours entirely lose their nitrogen-fixing activity.[356] Yet intact cells fix nitrogen over a wide pH range.

3. Light intensity

While light has little or no effect on nitrogen fixation by obligate heterotrophs it is obviously extremely important to nitrogen-fixing photosynthetic organisms, such as the photosynthetic bacteria and blue-green algae, for in these it makes available the energy, possibly the reducing power for fixation, and the carbon skeletons to accept the fixed nitrogen. This results in a close interdependence between nitrogen fixation and photosynthesis as has been shown for *Anabaena cylindrica*[195] and for the photosynthetic bacterium *Chromatium*[25] in which fixation ceases abruptly when they are placed in the dark. The *Anabaena* data (Figs. 11 and 12) also show that high light intensities may specifically inhibit fixation, for example the optimum light intensities for nitrogen fixation and for photosynthesis are near to 5,500 and 10,000 metre candles respectively. It was also noted in *Anabaena* that at the higher light intensity the nitrogen-containing pigments phycocyanin and phycoerythrin decreased, while the non-nitrogenous carotenoids correspondingly increased.[195] Low light intensity inhibits fixation relative to growth, probably because of the resulting shortage of photosynthetic products. Thus, nitrogen fixation in whole cells is light-dependent and sensitive to the light intensity employed. The question then is: is it an obligate association? It now seems certain that it is not, for if a suitable organic substrate is provided certain phototrophs, for example, Allison's strain of *Nostoc muscorum*[304] and *Chlorogloea fritschii*[176] fix nitrogen in the dark, although the fixation rate is usually less than in the light. Also cell-free extracts of *Anabaena* fix nitrogen in the dark and fixation may actually be inhibited in the light.[130] In cell-free extracts of *Rhodospirillum rubrum* the fixation rate is similar in the light and in the dark.[462] Thus the overall tentative conclusion appears to be that nitrogen fixation is not specifically light-dependent, even in obligate phototrophs, as long as a supply of carbon skeletons, reducing power, and energy is available.

From the above evidence it seems general that the nitrogen-fixing systems of free-living organisms, like those of symbiotic nitrogen-fixing plants, are more sensitive to extremes of physical conditions than are the respiratory or photosynthetic systems. The reasons for this are unknown, but it is likely to be an

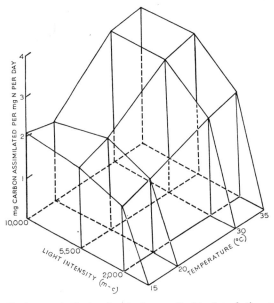

FIG. 11. Carbon assimilation by *Anabaena cylindrica* in relation to light and temperature (after ref. 195).

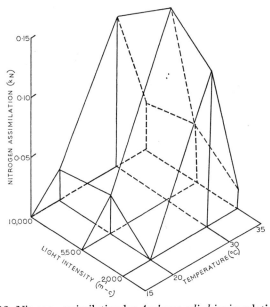

FIG. 12. Nitrogen assimilation by *Anabaena cylindrica* in relation to light and temperature (after ref. 195).

important consideration in ecological studies on these organisms, for as can be seen, it does not necessarily follow that because the organisms are growing they are actively fixing nitrogen.

7.3 Inorganic ions and nitrogen fixation

As the rate of nitrogen fixation in whole cells closely parallels the growth rate of the organism, all the nutrients essential for growth will also be required indirectly for fixation. These requirements are entirely inorganic as far as the nitrogen-fixing Myxophyceae are concerned, but certain bacteria require organic growth factors such as *para*-aminobenzoic acid or biotin. These are probably not specifically associated with fixation, although as mentioned previously biotin stimulates the formation of the nitrogenase system in some strains of *Pseudomonas*.[433] The nutrients which have been most extensively studied are cobalt, molybdenum and iron.

1. *Cobalt*

The discovery of a cobalt requirement by plants was first made in 1954 when the element was shown to be essential for the growth of blue-green algae on elemental nitrogen and on combined nitrogen.[266] More recently Kliewer and Evans[298] showed that little growth of *Azotobacter* occurred on elemental nitrogen in the absence of cobalt, but that as little as 0.001 parts per 10^9 allowed optimum fixation, while 1,000 parts per 10^9 were inhibitory. Thus it was established to be essential for growth but only in small amounts. The next point was—is it specifically required for nitrogen fixation? When this was tested by supplying the organism with, and without cobalt, in the presence and absence of combined nitrogen growth was always better when cobalt was added. However, the cobalt requirement was less when combined nitrogen was supplied indicating that the element was essential for growth, and that there was an additional requirement for fixation. There was a direct correlation between the quantities of cobalt added and the amounts of vitamin B_{12} coenzyme synthesized by the organism, just as in symbiotic nodules and rhizobia. Nicholas and his co-workers have obtained rather similar results with *Azotobacter*[385] and have demonstrated a cobalt requirement for nitrogen fixation, hydrogenase activity, nitrite reductases and for hydroxylamine reductases in *Clostridium*.[383]

2. Molybdenum

Ever since the finding in 1930 by Bortels[84] that *Azotobacter* required molybdenum for growth on elemental nitrogen the rôle of this element in relation to nitrogen fixation has been extensively investigated, and Bortels' findings have been confirmed many times by other workers for other organisms. For example, *Beijerinckia* requires 0·004–0·034 parts per million of molybdenum for half-optimal growth on elemental nitrogen and ten times less for growth on nitrate nitrogen.[42] Thus there is a distinct requirement for nitrate assimilation and an additional requirement for fixation. In many organisms, such as *Aerobacter*[419] and *Beijerinckia*[42] a requirement for growth on ammonium-nitrogen has not been established. The data on blue-green algae are rather conflicting, for although there is evidence of a greater requirement for growth on gaseous nitrogen[601] other workers found the requirement for optimum growth on elemental and nitrate nitrogen to be similar (0·1 parts per million).[23,403] Although such discrepancies in the overall picture exist, the weight of evidence suggests that in nitrogen-fixing organisms, molybdenum is required for growth on nitrate nitrogen and that there is an additional requirement when the organism is fixing nitrogen.

A second piece of evidence which indicates a dual rôle for molybdenum is that in some, but not all, organisms vanadium can replace molybdenum when they are fixing nitrogen but not when they are growing on nitrate nitrogen.[42] This suggests that there are at least two sites of molybdenum activity, one associated with fixation, the other with nitrate assimilation. In nitrogen fixation, molybdenum is probably involved in the nitrogenase system, for Nicholas found, both with *Clostridium* and *Azotobacter*, that although hydrogenase activity was vigorous when either vanadium or molybdenum was supplied, nitrogen fixation was reduced when molybdenum was absent and that

vanadium could not substitute for it.[379] It has also been suggested[467-8] that hydrogenase is a molybdo-flavoprotein but it
seems more likely to be an iron-flavoprotein (see next para-
graph). In either case molybdenum is present in the nitrogen-
fixing particles found in the supernatant of cell-free extracts of
Azotobacter vinelandii and there probably functions in the electron
transport chain concerned with the reduction of elemental
nitrogen.[380]

3. *Iron*

It has been shown that iron is essential for nitrogen fixation in
symbiotic organisms, and that one of its functions there is in
haemoglobin synthesis. A similar function is unlikely in free-
living organisms, which apparently do not contain the pigment.
There is no doubt, however, from the usual lines of evidence
that iron is implicated in the fixation process, for example,
Azotobacter cells growing on elemental nitrogen have a higher
iron requirement than have those growing on combined nitrogen.[167] Also, carbon monoxide, which combines with ferrous
iron, inhibits growth in nitrogen-free medium at partial pressures
a hundred times less than those necessary to inhibit growth on
combined nitrogen.[551] As with molybdenum, iron is associated
with the nitrogen-fixing particles found in cell-free extracts of
Azotobacter.[380]

As iron is thus obviously associated with fixation what is its
rôle in the process? It has been suggested that in *Azotobacter*[379]
and *Clostridium*[417] it is a component of the hydrogenase system,
for example Nicholas has shown, as can be seen from Table 8,
that hydrogenase activity is reduced to a greater extent than is
nitrogenase activity when iron is limiting while the opposite is
the case when molybdenum is limiting.

There is also recent evidence that in some nitrogen-fixing
micro-organisms at least, part of the iron is present in the form
of the non-haem iron protein ferredoxin (Fd). Ferredoxin is the
name given to a non-haem electron carrier first isolated from
Clostridium pasteurianum in 1962,[364] although a similar type substance had earlier been obtained from whole spinach leaves[454]
and from the bacterium *Chromatium*.[324a] It is probably the most
electro-negative electron carrier so far isolated from plants and

has a molecular weight of 5,000–6,000. In the oxidized state it is brown with absorption maxima at 280 mμ, 300 mμ, and 390 mμ, but it is colourless when reduced.[357,361] The reactive part of the molecule contains seven iron atoms, all of which are probably in the ferric state, bonded by sulphur bridges, and five amide groups are present.[65,300] Recently a red protein with an absorption spectrum rather similar to the cobamide coenzymes found in symbiotic nitrogen-fixing nodules has been found associated with ferredoxin.[359]

TABLE 8. The effect of iron and molybdenum on hydrogenase and nitrogenase activity in *Azotobacter vinelandii* (Strain O) (after ref. 379)

Medium	Complete	Minus Iron	Minus molybdenum
Hydrogenase (QH$_2$/mg N$_2$/hr)	4,620	1,150	4,150
Total nitrogen fixed (mg/l.)	125	75	52
Dry weight yields as per cent of normal	100	35	70

Ferredoxin has been shown to be an essential for fixation in several experiments[358,360] including one which showed that the nitrogen-fixing activity of cell-free extracts of *Clostridium* is lost if a ferredoxin fraction is separated off, but that reactivation occurs (though not to the full extent) if pure ferredoxin is added (see Fig. 15, p. 110). The incomplete reactivation suggests that the separated ferredoxin fraction must also contain some other substance which stimulates fixation. It is thought that ferredoxin acts in the nitrogen-fixing process by transferring electrons from a hydrogen-donating system to the nitrogenase system thus bringing about the reduction of nitrogen. This aspect is discussed later in 8.7. It should be emphasized that although ferredoxin is necessary for fixation to occur in certain anaerobes it is not solely associated with the fixation of nitrogen, for ferredoxin occurs in non-nitrogen-fixing organisms in several electron transferring systems.[34,357,454,503-4] Indeed it may well be shown to be a multifunctional electron transport protein of universal occurrence in plants.

7.4 The effect of various gases on nitrogen fixation

As can be seen from the preceding section it is often possible to obtain more detailed information on the effects of various factors on fixation by studying free-living organisms rather than symbiotic systems. This similarly applies to the effects of various gases on fixation. The general conclusions arrived at from higher plant studies have been confirmed with free-living organisms, and here only the major differences between the two groups, and data which provide additional information, need be included.

1. *Nitrogen*

Studies by the Wisconsin school have shown that the K_{N_2} values for free-living nitrogen-fixing organisms are similar to those obtained for sliced legume nodules,[107] being of the order of 0·02 atm. for *Azotobacter* and for *Nostoc*.[109] In the case of the blue-green alga it has been pointed out that this value is provisional because of the large variation in the results obtained. Thus, nitrogen should never be a factor limiting fixation in ordinary air. This is particularly important in the case of an unidentified nitrogen-fixing bacterium isolated from jute fields[449] for this organism can apparently grow only on elemental nitrogen. Why this should be the case is difficult to understand.

2. *Hydrogen*

Molecular hydrogen is a specific and competitive inhibitor of nitrogen fixation in symbiotic nitrogen-fixing plants and has a similar effect on nitrogen-fixing micro-organisms. However in anaerobic species, which may evolve hydrogen during metabolism, high partial pressures of hydrogen are required to bring this inhibition about, for example in *Bacillus polymyxa* fixation still occurs at a pH_2 of 0·5 atm., though to a much lesser extent than in a hydrogen-free atmosphere.[230] A possible reason for this inhibition is discussed later (8.7). Hydrogen is without effect on nitrogen-fixing organisms when they are growing on combined nitrogen. On the other hand, both elemental nitrogen and ammonium-nitrogen, even in low concentrations, inhibit the evolution of hydrogen, for example in photosynthetic nitrogen-fixing bacteria growing on amino-nitrogen,[290,377] suggesting that the hydrogen is used up in the reduction of gaseous nitrogen to ammonia, and in the formation of amino acids from ammonia. Also, in cell-free extracts of *Chromatium* and *Clostridium*, molecular hydrogen, instead of being inhibitory to nitrogen fixation, may actually act as a source of electrons in the nitrogen-fixing process. Aspects of hydrogen metabolism in relation to nitrogen fixation are dealt with in 8.7.

3. *Oxygen*

As both strict aerobes and strict anaerobes are known to fix nitrogen, it seems unlikely that oxygen is an essential requirement for fixation. It is more likely that in aerobic organisms it is necessary only for general metabolism. Several lines of evidence support this point of view. First, if a reductive pathway leading to the formation of ammonia is envisaged (as will be seen in 8.3 most evidence points to this) oxygen need not be involved. Secondly, in whole cells of *Azotobacter* and the blue-green algae, high oxygen concentrations depress fixation rather than stimulate it. Thirdly, air (or oxygen) inhibits nitrogen fixation in cell-free extracts of the blue-green alga *Anabaena cylindrica*.[130] In both organisms air inhibits the hydrogenase system,[95,206] the nitrogenase at least in *Azotobacter* being stable in air.[95] Fourthly, it has been shown that the nitrogenase of *Azotobacter* fixes nitrogen under reducing conditions. The data thus support the contention that oxygen plays no direct rôle in the fixation of nitrogen and suggest that the process of nitrogen fixation may first have become established under the reducing conditions of the primitive Earth's atmosphere.

4. *Carbon monoxide*

Free-living nitrogen-fixing organisms are less sensitive to carbon monoxide than are symbiotic systems, the concentrations necessary to inhibit fixation being ten to a hundred times greater. This is conceivably due to the absence of haemoglobin in free-living systems but other iron enzymes are undoubtedly present. Fixation is affected specifically and competitively, as can be seen from data on the blue-green alga *Nostoc muscorum*, in which fixation is inhibited at a partial pressure of carbon monoxide of $0 \cdot 0015$ atm., a concentration which is without effect on the uptake of combined nitrogen; also the inhibitory effect is more pronounced in the presence of a pN_2 of $0 \cdot 10$ atm. than at a pN_2 of $0 \cdot 75$ atm.[109] Cell-free extract studies on *Clostridium* have confirmed the data obtained with whole cells but have shown in addition that hydrogenase activity, pyruvic acid dehydrogenase activity and some part of the nitrogenase system are all inhibited.[357] As these enzymes are involved in nitrogen fixation (see 8.7) it is not surprising that carbon monoxide inhibits fixation in whole cells.

7.5 The effect of combined nitrogen on fixation

It is known from studies on symbiotic systems that combined nitrogen inhibits nitrogen fixation, the extent of inhibition being, on the whole, inversely proportional to the amount of combined nitrogen supplied. With higher plants it is difficult to obtain data readily on the short-term effects of combined nitrogen on fixation and free-living organisms have provided more information on this aspect.

With the exception of one species of bacterium[449] all nitrogen-fixing organisms utilize ammonium- and nitrate nitrogen. When ammonium-nitrogen is supplied it is assimilated immediately as can be seen from Fig. 13, indicating that ammonia lies on the nitrogen-fixing pathway and that the enzyme system is already adapted to its use. Although fixation is partially inhibited by very low concentrations of ammonium-nitrogen, higher concentrations are necessary for complete inhibition,[494, 610] for example in the blue-green alga *Calothrix* 50 mg per litre of ammonium-nitrogen causes 89 per cent inhibition.[494] It has also been reported[27] that high concentrations of ammonium-nitrogen inhibit respiration but this may be an indirect effect due to changes in the internal pH of the cells. There is some evidence from studies on *Pseudomonas* that ammonium-nitrogen not only inhibits the functioning of the nitrogenase system but that it also inhibits its formation, for on transferring cells from ammonium-nitrogen to molecular nitrogen there is a lag of up to 10 hours before fixation re-commences.[432]

Although ammonium-nitrogen is utilized immediately this is not the case when nitrate nitrogen is supplied. Here, as can be seen from Fig. 13, a period of adaptation is necessary before assimilation occurs suggesting that the nitrate must be first reduced to ammonia, and that nitrate reductase is an adaptive enzyme. Nitrate-nitrogen inhibits fixation in the majority of

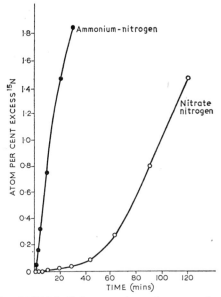

FIG. 13. Uptake of ^{15}N-labelled ammonium-nitrogen and nitrate-nitrogen by *Azotobacter vinelandii* with time (after ref. 111).

organisms in low concentrations, the noted exception being *Anabaena cylindrica* where high nitrate-nitrogen concentrations are necessary for inhibition.[10] The effect of nitrite-nitrogen on fixation appears to be complex. It was first reported by Federov[179] to stimulate fixation and Azim and Roberts[29] obtained similar results. It was found that on transferring *Azotobacter* into 10^{-5}M nitrite fixation was inhibited. However the alga completely assimilated the nitrite in thirty minutes, and then fixation not only restarted but the rate increased markedly so that after 4 hours it was 40 per cent greater than in untreated cells.

The effects of various other nitrogen compounds on fixation

have been studied by several workers. With the exception of urea, which markedly inhibits fixation,[126] the compounds tested have generally been those suspected of being intermediates in the fixation pathway, and their effects on fixation are discussed later in 8.2 and 8.3.

8 Biochemistry of Nitrogen Fixation

8.1

Although nitrogen fixation is restricted to a small minority of plants these do not differ markedly from their non-nitrogen-fixing counterparts. Morphologically one cannot differentiate between nitrogen-fixing and non-nitrogen-fixing bacteria, nor between nodulated plants growing on elemental nitrogen or combined nitrogen. Similarly from a biochemical viewpoint nitrogen-fixing and non-nitrogen-fixing species are similar except that the former have in addition a set of enzymes by which they perform the extremely useful and important function of fixing molecular nitrogen from the atmosphere. It is the pathway leading from elemental nitrogen to its incorporation into organic combination which is of particular interest to the biochemist, who has to consider: (1) the initial combination of the nitrogen molecule with other substances, (2) the substance or substances formed immediately before the nitrogen enters organic combination, (3) the intermediates between the above two steps, and (4) the enzymic mechanisms involved. Each of these will be dealt with in turn.

8.2 The initial entry of molecular nitrogen into combination

Theoretically there are four possible ways in which combination can occur: the nitrogen can be reduced, oxidized, hydrolysed, or combine directly with organic molecules. Unlike nitrogen-fixing plants, man has not been able to induce any of these reactions to occur at room temperature. The use of inhibitors in the hope that free intermediates would accumulate and thus give some clue to the reaction sequence has been almost entirely unsuccessful and it seems that there are no such intermediates, the reactions in question taking place on the enzyme surfaces.

A second approach has been to construct hypothetical pathways and to feed the suspected intermediates to the organism and to determine whether these are utilized, or whether fixation has been specifically affected. This latter method has been frequently used, but again not with much success. It seems most likely however that the molecular nitrogen enters combination either by a process of oxidation or reduction.

1. *Entry by oxidation*

It would be expected that if the initial step were oxidative the first formed product would have an oxidation level akin to that of nitrous oxide (N_2O) or some related compound such as nitramide (H_2N-NO_2), or hyponitrous acid ($HON=NOH$).

Nitrous oxide has been shown to be a specific competitive inhibitor of fixation by *Azotobacter*.[443] This suggests that it is an intermediate, but unfortunately one cannot be sure whether it is actually utilized. According to Mozen and Burris[369] ^{15}N-labelled nitrous oxide is slowly utilized by *Azotobacter*, but others[593] have been unable to confirm this and suggest[445] that the nitrogen assimilated may actually have been labelled molecular nitrogen formed by dissociation of the nitrous oxide. Nitramide is difficult to test as it decomposes rapidly in solution, but when undecomposed nitramide was fed to *Azotobacter* over an appreciable period there was no utilization.[368] There is no experimental evidence that hyponitrous acid is an intermediate, for it is a general poison.[123] This latter finding of course does not mean that it is not an intermediate for as pointed out by Steward and Pollard[501] there are many substances present in plant cells in concentrations which if supplied exogenously would kill the plant off, for example the concentrations of iodine in the brown alga *Laminaria*. The recent finding[181] that *Anabaena* reduces nitric oxide (NO) when fed on molecular nitrogen or nitrate, but not on ammonium-nitrogen, suggests that in this organism nitric oxide may be an intermediate in an oxidative pathway.

Because the results have been mainly negative there is no oxidative scheme which can clearly be considered more likely than the others. In all, hydroxylamine (NH_2OH) has been considered as the end-product, not only on the basis of its molecular structure but also, as will be seen later, because there is some evidence that it is an intermediate. The obvious possibilities can be summarized as follows:

1. $N_2 \longrightarrow N_2O \longrightarrow H_2N-NO_2 \longrightarrow 2NH_2OH$
   nitrous oxide   nitramide   hydroxylamine

or

2. $N_2 \longrightarrow N_2O \longrightarrow HON=NOH \longrightarrow 2NH_2OH$
   hyponitrous acid

or

3. $N_2 \longrightarrow N_2O \longrightarrow 2NO \longrightarrow 2NH_2OH$
   nitric oxide

The recent finding that the nitrogenase from the aerobe *Azotobacter* fixes nitrogen anaerobically when supplied with *Clostridium* hydrogenase[95] suggests that an aerobic step in the actual fixation pathway is unnecessary and makes the reductive pathway more likely. Whether this applies to all nitrogen-fixing aerobes remains to be seen.

2. *Entry by reduction*

If the initial step is reductive the first products will probably be closely related to diimide (HN=NH), to hydrazine (N_2H_4), or some similar substance which is then reduced to ammonia.

Although diimide is a theoretical possibility it is known to be extremely labile, and all attempts to prepare it chemically have failed. More attention has been focused on hydrazine[101,209-10, 502] which generally has been found to be a non-specific inhibitor of fixation. This, together with the fact that when unlabelled hydrazine is added to cell-free extracts of *Clostridium* which had been fixing ^{15}N-labelled molecular nitrogen, and then recovered, it remains unlabelled[209-10] is evidence against it being an intermediate. However, very low concentrations have been reported to stimulate fixation[28] so that the quantities supplied may be critical. Furthermore Bach[32] has obtained interesting evidence which suggests that it may, in fact, be an intermediate. He found that when *Azotobacter* was supplied with hydrazine over 50 per cent of the nitrogen assimilated was incorporated into organic azines. One of these, also found in soya bean

nodules, was chromatographically indistinguishable from di-
hydropyridazinone-5-carboxylic acid (PCA) which is formed at
room temperature by the reaction between hydrazine and α-
ketoglutarate. This suggests that in the plant molecular nitrogen
is incorporated into hydrazine and then into azines such as PCA
as follows:

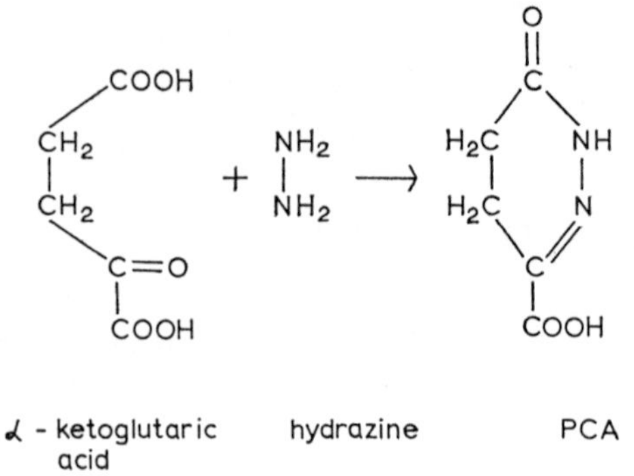

| α - ketoglutaric acid | hydrazine | PCA |

Furthermore as the rate of hydrazine uptake is reduced in
the presence of ammonium-nitrogen, and as the ^{15}N-enrichment
of PCA is approximately three hundred times as much when the
organism is grown on ^{15}N-labelled molecular nitrogen than
when it is grown on ^{15}N-labelled ammonium-nitrogen this suggests that these organic azines may be intermediates between
hydrazine and ammonia.

An alternative pathway is possibly via hydroxylamine which
is then reduced to ammonia. Blom suggested in 1931 that
hydroxylamine may be an intermediate,[64] a suggestion followed
up by Virtanen and his co-workers, who detected aspartic acid
and oximes as excretory products of legume roots[548a] and suggested that this finding could be readily explained by the
following reactions:

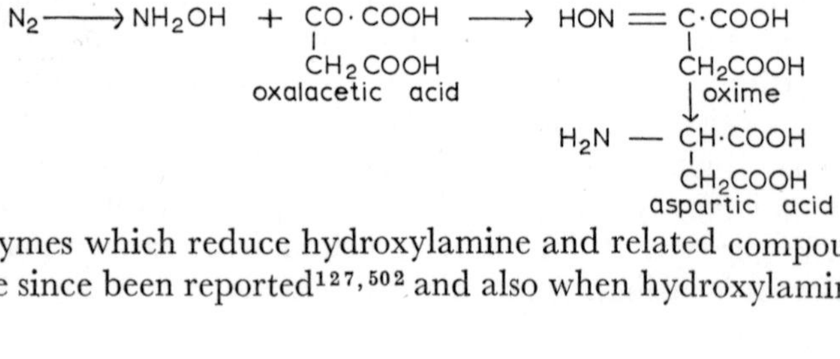

Enzymes which reduce hydroxylamine and related compounds
have since been reported[127, 502] and also when hydroxylamine is

supplied at low concentration it is utilized by certain nitrogen-fixing organisms, including *Anabaena cylindrica*. In this alga[245] hydroxylamine reductase is an adaptive enzyme and is formed when the organism is grown on molecular nitrogen but not when it is grown on ammonium-nitrogen or glutamate, thus suggesting that hydroxylamine is an intermediate between molecular nitrogen and ammonia. This is also supported by the finding that when *Anabaena* is supplied with hydroxylamine, the hydroxylamine may be recovered almost quantitatively as ammonia.[244] Furthermore, when the organism is grown on nitrate or molecular nitrogen the level of hydroxylamine reductase is similar, thus suggesting that hydroxylamine is a common intermediate in nitrogen fixation and nitrate reduction.[245]

On the other hand there is evidence against the hydroxylamine hypothesis. First, unlabelled hydroxylamine does not become labelled when it is added to and then recovered from cell-free extracts which previously had been fixing ^{15}N-labelled molecular nitrogen.[209-10] Secondly, hydroxylamine has been found in the medium in which *Azotobacter* has been growing, whether the nitrogen source is molecular nitrogen or ammonium-nitrogen.[551] Thirdly, in this organism, unlike *Anabaena cylindrica*, hydroxylamine reductase formation is stimulated in the presence of nitrate but not molecular nitrogen.[481] Hydroxylamine is also extremely toxic and there is little evidence that plants actually grow on it,[391] but as mentioned earlier this does not mean it is not an intermediate.

The reductive pathways for which most evidence has been obtained may be summarized as follows:

1) $N_2 \longrightarrow N_2H_2 \longrightarrow N_2H_4$ ⟶ organic azines such as PCA
                                      ↘ $2NH_3$

2) $N_2 \longrightarrow N_2H_2 \longrightarrow 2NH_2OH \longrightarrow 2NH_3$

Thus the end-product in the inorganic reduction of nitrogen would be either hydrazine or ammonia. Although diimide is suggested here as a hypothetical intermediate, the recent suggestion of Winter and Burris[596] that azodicarboxylic acid rather than diimide is possibly the intermediate should be borne in mind.

8.3 The key intermediate

Having considered possibilities for the early intermediates let us now consider what is known about the key intermediate. This has been defined by Wilson and Burris[586] as 'the compound which represents the end of the fixation reaction and the start of assimilation of fixed nitrogen into the organic carbon skeleton'. Three main possibilities suggest themselves. These are: hydroxylamine, hydrazine, and ammonia.

1. *Hydroxylamine*

The suggestion that hydroxylamine is the key intermediate was first made by Virtanen in 1938,[540] largely on the basis of the finding of aspartic acid in the medium in which nodulated legumes were growing—a finding, as already mentioned, most readily explained by assuming a reaction between hydroxylamine and oxalacetic acid. However, with the later discovery that glutamic acid was also an excretory product,[542] this theory was modified, and it was then suggested that the formation of aspartic acid from hydroxylamine was a by-reaction and that the hydroxylamine was probably reduced to ammonia which then combined with α-ketoglutarate as follows:

$$\begin{array}{c} \text{CO·COOH} \\ | \\ \text{CH}_2 \\ | \\ \text{CH}_2\text{COOH} \\ \alpha\text{-ketoglutaric} \\ \text{acid} \end{array} + \text{NH}_3 \xrightarrow[\substack{\text{glutamic acid} \\ \text{dehydrogenase}}]{(2H)} \begin{array}{c} \text{NH}_2\text{CH·COOH} \\ | \\ \text{CH}_2 \\ | \\ \text{CH}_2\text{COOH} \\ \text{glutamic} \\ \text{acid} \end{array} + \text{H}_2\text{O}$$

Later still, with the accumulation of evidence against hydroxylamine (see 8.2) Virtanen abandoned his earlier hypotheses, stating in 1963 that there is 'no longer any evidence for hydroxylamine as a direct intermediate in nitrogen fixation'.[551] However, few authorities will go as far as to say that hydroxylamine is not an intermediate at all. On the contrary, some substance of similar oxidation-reduction level is necessary in the fixation pathway, irrespective of whether molecular nitrogen enters by an oxidative or reductive pathway, and the Wisconsin workers who advocate ammonia as the key intermediate include hydroxylamine in their scheme. What is now generally accepted is that it is not the *key* intermediate.

2. *Ammonia*

While the 'hydroxylamine as key intermediate' hypothesis has undergone such modification and criticism that it is now almost, if not entirely, dead and buried, the 'ammonia as key intermediate' theory has gone from strength to strength. As noted above, Virtanen suggested on the discovery that glutamic acid was an excretory product that it was probably formed by the reaction between ammonia and α-ketoglutarate, in which case ammonia would be key intermediate. This suggestion had previously been elaborated upon by Burris and Wilson.[108]

It had also been suggested as early as 1926 that ammonia was a product of nitrogen fixation when it was found in medium in which *Azotobacter* had been grown.[302] However it was probably autolytic in origin rather than excretory.[99,100] The major evidence supporting the ammonia hypothesis can be summarized as follows:

1. When nitrogen-fixing cell-free extracts are supplied with ^{15}N-labelled molecular nitrogen the first formed detectable product is ammonia, the labelled ammonia recovered being equivalent to the labelled nitrogen assimilated.[362] Similarly in detached root nodules of soya bean exposed to ^{15}N-labelled molecular nitrogen, more than 90 per cent of the soluble fixed nitrogen can be accounted for as ammonia after one minute's exposure.[55] In intact micro-organisms the highest labelling is found in glutamic acid, aspartic acid and ammonia.[584] The high labelling of glutamic acid is readily explained if one accepts that ammonia is formed first and combines with α-ketoglutaric acid in the presence of glutamic acid dehydrogenase as indicated earlier. The aspartic acid is then formed from glutamic acid by transamination.

2. Nitrogen fixation is immediately inhibited when ammonium-nitrogen is added to cultures of nitrogen-fixing organisms and the ammonium-nitrogen is preferentially assimilated.[378]

3. When *Clostridium*,[611] or the nitrogen-fixing blue-green alga *Westelliopsis prolifica*,[415] is exposed to ^{15}N-labelled gaseous nitrogen, ammonia highly labelled with ^{15}N comprises the bulk of the extracellular nitrogen produced during the early stages of fixation (see 5.6 and 6.7).

4. When nitrogen-fixing organisms are supplied for a short period with ^{15}N-labelled molecular nitrogen, or ^{15}N-labelled ammonium-nitrogen and the distribution of heavy nitrogen within the constituent amino acids analysed, the relative quantitative distribution in each series is very similar.[557,584]

3. *Hydrazine*

If, as discussed on p. 100, hydrazine does combine with α-ketoglutarate to form PCA, or a related substance, hydrazine would be the key intermediate. According to Bach[32] the PCA is likely to be reduced to glutamine. However other possibilities are that hydrazine forms ammonia directly or that it combines with water to give hydroxylamine and ammonia as follows:

$$N_2H_4 + H_2O \rightarrow NH_2OH + NH_3$$

There is no experimental evidence for this. However, if either were correct, hydrazine would not be the key intermediate, and the formation of PCA could still be explained on the basis that it is formed by side-reactions not directly concerned with the main nitrogen-fixing pathway.

The possible schemes to include ammonia, hydroxylamine and hydrazine are summarized in Fig. 14. Evidence accumulated to date makes it almost certain that the key intermediate is

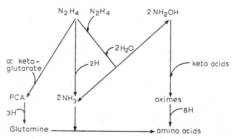

Fig. 14. Possible interrelations of suspected intermediates in nitrogen fixation (after ref. 380).

ammonia—not hydroxylamine or hydrazine. Further discussion on the mechanism of fixation in this book assumes this to be the case.

Hypothetical though these pathways may be, it is evident that basically, and irrespective of which, if any, of the above schemes is correct there are three major requirements necessary for fixation to occur. These are: a source of reducing power, an energy source, and appropriate enzyme systems. To allow the process to continue for any length of time there must also be carbon skeletons to accept the fixed nitrogen. These factors will now be considered.

8.4 Source of reducing power

The reduction of molecular nitrogen is the characteristic feature of the fixation process and evidence, obtained mainly from free-living nitrogen-fixing organisms, indicates that there are at least three possible sources of reducing power: pyruvate, molecular hydrogen, and in the case of photosynthetic organisms direct photoreduction.

1. *Pyruvate*

The ability of pyruvate to serve as an ultimate source of reducing power for fixation suggested itself when it was found to be the only additive necessary for fixation in cell-free extracts of *Clostridium pasteurianum*.[117-8] No other additives could completely replace pyruvate in this organism, although α-keto-butyrate could partially substitute for it. The substitution of α-ketobutyrate for pyruvate is possible in several other systems as well. Pyruvate has similarly been shown to be necessary for fixation in cell-free extracts of organisms other than *Clostridium* (see Table 7, p. 79). Thus all the enzymes, co-enzymes etc. required for its production will be indirectly required for fixation to proceed. Although pyruvate serves as reductant, the requirement does not appear to be specifically for this substance as fixation does not begin in cell-free extracts until a considerable quantity of pyruvate has been consumed[362] and also the amount of nitrogen fixed in relation to pyruvate consumed is small, being of the order 44–100 moles of pyruvate consumed per mole of gaseous nitrogen fixed.[363] It is now certain that pyruvate functions in the phosphoroclastic reaction:

$$CH_3CO.COOH + H_3PO_4 \rightarrow CH_3(CO)H_2PO_4 + CO_2 + H_2$$

producing acetyl phosphate, carbon dioxide and hydrogen. The source of electrons necessary for reduction could, as a result, conceivably be either molecular hydrogen itself, or electrons generated in this reaction. This also suggests that when extracts such as those of *Chromatium*, which have no pyruvate requirement, fix nitrogen, it may be because they utilize molecular hydrogen or some other reductant, or that they have an endogenous supply of pyruvate.

2. *Molecular hydrogen*

The first evidence that molecular hydrogen could act as a source of electrons was obtained by Arnon and his collaborators in 1960[25] when they observed that if cell-free extracts of *Chromatium* were supplied in the dark with 0·5 atm. molecular nitrogen enriched with 96 atom per cent excess ^{15}N for 2 hours, the extract showed an enrichment of 0·0274 atom per cent excess ^{15}N at the end of the experiment, while, when an addition of 0·5 atm. hydrogen was also added the atom per cent excess ^{15}N was 0·0430.[25] Thus, fixation was stimulated by molecular hydrogen. Other workers, using a variety of organisms, were at first unable to obtain fixation when molecular hydrogen was used as reductant, and it was considered a possibility that the initial reduction of molecular nitrogen required electrons of greater potential than could be supplied by molecular hydrogen. It seemed that the stimulation observed could be due to molecular hydrogen serving as a source of electrons for steps other than the initial reduction, leaving the electrons of greater potential available for the reduction of nitrogen.[357]

However, the ability of molecular hydrogen to act as a source of electrons has been confirmed for *Clostridium pasteurianum*.[358] It was found that cell-free extracts fixed nitrogen as rapidly on molecular hydrogen as on pyruvate, providing that a source of high energy phosphate (acetyl phosphate) was available and the extract contained a high protein content (up to 22 mg protein per ml of reaction mixture). Recently it has been shown that in cell-free extracts of *Azotobacter* and *Rhodospirillum* molecular hydrogen does not act as a reductant although sodium dithionite does.[96]

3. *Photoreduction of nitrogen*

In 1956 Gest and his co-workers discovered that in photosynthetic bacteria the photo-evolution of hydrogen was completely inhibited by molecular nitrogen or ammonia although it occurred when the cells were grown on glutamate.[219] They suggested that photoreduction of nitrogen by electrons produced on the photolysis of water may occur. This photoreduction theory has been elaborated by Arnon's school[25] who found that although *Chromatium* fixed nitrogen in the light when supplied with thiosulphate or succinate as exogenous electron donors, it was completely inhibited in the dark. A non-cyclic electron flow was therefore suggested in photosynthetic organisms in which electrons, supplied by exogenous electron donors, pass via cytochromes, to chlorophyll excited by light, and then on to gaseous nitrogen. Light-dependent nitrogen fixation has been confirmed in *Chromatium*[47] and in *Rhodospirillum rubrum*.[427] Evidence for the direct photoreduction of nitrogen has also been obtained from experiments on the blue-green alga *Anabaena cylindrica*. Under certain conditions this alga evolves more oxygen when growing on molecular nitrogen than when growing on ammonium-nitrogen and this 'extra' oxygen may be accounted for, in the absence of carbon dioxide, if the nitrogen is reduced to ammonia according to the following equation:[195]

$$N_2 + 3H_2O \rightarrow 2NH_3 + 1\tfrac{1}{2}O_2$$

That is, photolysis of water may supply the reducing power directly. It has also been shown recently, however, that this evidence for photoreduction is not obtained under all experimental conditions,[130] and as a result the whole problem in *Anabaena* is not as clear-cut as was once thought. There is obviously a close interrelationship between photosynthesis and nitrogen fixation but at the same time fixation in some organisms at least is not light dependent. For example, certain blue-green algae fix nitrogen slowly in the dark if a suitable carbohydrate source is provided.[176,304] The complicated interrelations of nitrogen fixation, photosynthesis and respiration are emphasized not only by purely physiological studies but also by the finding that in cell-free extracts of *Anabaena*, the enzymes for all three processes are probably closely associated with the photosynthetic lamellae.[130] Further studies on cell-free extracts are required to determine exactly what these interrelations are.

8.5 Energy sources

Whether the overall process of nitrogen fixation requires energy or dissipates energy has been the subject of a good deal of controversy. Evidence for and against the overall process being endothermic has been obtained.[38] Irrespective of which is correct it seems certain that if diimide, hydrazine, or hydroxylamine, are formed from molecular nitrogen, energy will be required for their synthesis. This can be seen from the following data:[428]

$$N_2 + H_2 + 2H_2O = 2NH_2OHaq \qquad \Delta G = +102 \cdot 2 \text{ kcal}$$
$$2NH_2OHaq + H_2 = N_2H_4aq + 2H_2O \qquad \Delta G = -71 \cdot 6 \text{ kcal}$$

In plant reactions in general, energy is available as adenosine tri-phosphate (ATP) which may be derived indirectly by the oxidation of carbohydrate substrates, whether these be photosynthetic or exogenous, or in photosynthetic organisms also directly by photophosphorylation, that is, by the combination of inorganic phosphate with ADP using light energy. Early studies provided little experimental evidence that an energy source was required for fixation, for in numerous experiments with cell-free extracts[380] fixation occurred without the addition of ATP. Thus it either was not required, or if it was, an endogenous energy source must have been present. Furthermore, when ATP was added to *Clostridium* extracts, fixation instead of being stimulated, as might be expected if it played a rôle, was actually inhibited.[118] These results suggested there was no ATP requirement. However in 1962 evidence of an ATP requirement was obtained when it was shown that the concentrations of arsenate which completely suppress the formation of acetyl phosphate and thus indirectly the synthesis of ATP, inhibit the fixation of nitrogen as well.[336] Glucose also inhibited fixation, presumably by forming glucose-6-phosphate with the result that no ATP was available for nitrogen fixation. While this evidence suggested, but did not conclusively prove, that ATP was necessary, it has since been shown to be essential under certain conditions.[146,241,358] For example, Mortenson[358] has obtained the following evidence which suggests that ATP is essential for fixation in cell-free extracts of *Clostridium* when molecular hydrogen is the electron source: (1) Fixation occurs only when acetyl phosphate is added to the extract, which already contains an ATP: acetate phosphotransferase; (2) the requirement is not for acetyl phosphate alone, as ADP must be added before the acetyl phosphate is consumed; (3) approximately 90 per cent of the nitrogen-fixing activity is lost after 6–8 hours dialysis of the cell-free extracts, but 50 per cent of this can be recovered by the addition of ATP and Mg^{++}. The fact that the nitrogen-fixing activity was not restored completely suggests that some other factor was lost on dialysis. The requirement for ATP, and for ferredoxin, can be seen from the data of Mortenson reproduced in Fig. 15 (p. 110). As the ATP concentrations essential for fixation were very criticol, this may explain the inability of earlier workers to demonstrate an ATP requirement. It is obvious that in *Clostridium* the phosphoroclastic reaction is probably one of the most important reactions governing nitrogen fixation, for it can supply not only a source of electrons, but also the acetyl phosphate required for ATP synthesis. Recently ATP has been shown to be essential for nitrogen fixation by cell-free extracts of *Azotobacter* and *Rhodospirillum rubrum* when sodium dithionite is the electron donor.[96]

8.6 Carbon skeletons

The carbon skeletons necessary to form amino acids from the ammonia produced in fixation must similarly be derived from photosynthetic products or from exogenous carbohydrate. Although there are several possible points at which ammonia may enter organic combination, evidence from nitrogen-fixing organisms suggests three in particular. These are: (1) α-keto-glutarate, (2) pyruvate, and (3) the ornithine cycle. Evidence for α-ketoglutarate is based largely on the finding that when many nitrogen-fixing organisms are exposed to ^{15}N-labelled molecular nitrogen for a short time, the highest labelling is

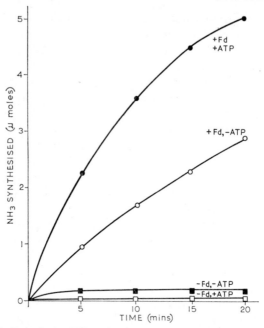

Fɪɢ. 15. Ferredoxin (Fd) and ᴀᴛᴘ, requirements for nitrogen fixation by cell-free extracts of *Clostridium pasteurianum* with H_2 as electron donor and acetyl phosphate as high-energy phosphate donor (after ref. 358).

found in glutamic acid.[584] For example in an experiment with *Clostridium pasteurianum* the most highly labelled compounds after 45 minutes exposure to ^{15}N-labelled nitrogen were glutamic acid, amide and ammonia, and alanine, these showing enrichments of 1·42, 0·62 and 0·62 atom per cent excess ^{15}N respectively.[611] Also, from cell-free extract studies, a high proportion of the ^{15}N incorporated during fixation is found in the ammonia fraction rather than in the amide fraction.[356] As glutamic acid is readily formed by reductive amination from ammonia and α-ketoglutarate (see p. 102) the latter would appear to be an important carbon skeleton and is probably formed from pyruvate via the Krebs' cycle. The former suggestion is backed up by the critical work of Sims and Folkes[472] who, using ^{15}N, showed that in the non-nitrogen fixing yeast *Candida utilis*, the only nitrogenous compounds to derive their α-amino nitrogen directly from ammonia were glutamic acid and glutamine. All other amino acids derive their α-amino nitrogen from glutamic acid, many of them by transamination.

Secondly pyruvate may act as carbon skeleton, combining with ammonia to form alanine in the presence of $NADH_2$ and a specific alanine dehydrogenase as follows:

$$CH_3CO.COOH + NH_3 \xrightarrow{NADH_2} CH_3CH(NH_2)COOH + H_2O$$

This reaction, first observed with *Bacillus subtilus*,[173,566] has been found by other workers in other micro-organisms. Recently it has been shown[94] that when ^{14}C-labelled carbon dioxide is supplied to the nitrogen-fixing organism *Chromatium* the ^{14}C accumulates first in pyruvate and then in the amino acids, aspartic acid, glutamic acid and alanine. Although entry via pyruvate appears possible in certain micro-organisms it is of much less widespread occurrence than the entry via α-ketoglutarate.

There is also the possibility that in certain plants the newly fixed ammonia enters organic combination via the ornithine cycle. It has been shown that if the nodules of the non-legume *Alnus* are exposed for 30 minutes to ^{15}N-labelled nitrogen and the free amino acids then extracted in 70 per cent alcohol, citrulline occurs in highest quantity and is one of the most highly labelled compound detected.[311] The labelling of the carbamyl group of this compounds with ^{15}N is also much higher than the labelling of the ammonia and glutamic acid. This suggests that the ammonia is incorporated into carbamyl phosphate as follows:

$$CO_2 + \overset{*}{N}H_3 + \text{ATP} \rightarrow \overset{*}{N}H_2.COO \sim ⑨ + \text{ADP}$$

the carbamyl phosphate then combining with ornithine to give citrulline, thus:

CH₂NH₂ — CH₂ — CH₂ — CH·NH₂ — COOH   ornithine

$+ \quad \overset{*}{N}H_2 \cdot COO \sim ⑨ \longrightarrow$

CH₂HNCON$\overset{*}{H}_2$ — CH₂ — CH₂ — CH·NH₂ — COOH   citrulline

$+ \quad ⑨OH$

Also in certain blue-green algae, after short exposures to ^{14}C-labelled carbon dioxide, highest radioactivity is found in citrulline. In *Nostoc muscorum*, for example, over 20 per cent of the labelling was found in citrulline after five minutes exposure to the radioactive isotope.[322] Although this may be a pathway in *Alnus* and possibly in blue-green algae, there is evidence that in *Clostridium* carbamyl phosphate does not act as an intermediate in fixation.[596] Thus it seems that the route from molecular nitrogen to its incorporation into organic combination is via ammonia and then in the majority of nitrogen-fixing species but not necessarily exclusively in all of them, via α-ketoglutarate to glutamic acid.

8.7 Nitrogenase and Hydrogenase

Having dealt with the source of reducing power, the energy requirements and the possible sources of carbon skeletons, it now remains to consider the enzyme systems. The main two are nitrogenase and hydrogenase.

Nitrogenase is the name given to the enzyme or enzyme system which catalyses the reduction of molecular nitrogen, possibly by electrons made available on the oxidation of reduced ferredoxin. Although such an enzyme system must exist, its nature is almost unknown. As mentioned earlier (p. 90) it is probably a molybdo-flavoprotein, an iron-flavoprotein, or a combination of both.

Hydrogenase reversibly catalyses the conversion of hydrogen ions to molecular hydrogen and has been detected in all nitrogen-fixing groups so far examined. Until recently it was reported as absent in the Myxophyceae but it is now known to be present in hydrogen-adapted cells of *Anabaena cylindrica*.[205-6]

Some of the evidence that hydrogenase is associated with fixation is as follows: (1) hydrogenase activity is greatest when the cells are growing on molecular nitrogen and is reduced when they are growing on combined nitrogen;[231] (2) molecular hydrogen inhibits nitrogen fixation both in aerobes[589,605-6] and anaerobes;[418] (3) the evolution of molecular hydrogen by photosynthetic bacteria is inhibited by elemental nitrogen or ammonia;[220,290,377] (4) hydrogenase activity is low in non-nitrogen-fixing bacterial mutants;[232] (5) a crude *Clostridium* hydrogenase system will support fixation by *Azotobacter* nitrogenase.[95] It should be noted however that there is no evidence that the *Azotobacter* hydrogenase will support nitrogen fixation by the *Azotobacter* nitrogenase.[96]

The nature of hydrogenase is uncertain. Shug *et al.*[467] partially purified the *Clostridium* hydrogenase and observed that on treating it with 70 per cent ammonium sulphate and dialysing, the supernatant had lost almost all its hydrogenase activity, but that this could be restored by the addition of flavine-adenine-dinucleotide (FAD) plus molybdenum. It was suggested on this evidence, and on comparison with other work, that even although additions of flavins alone did not stimulate activity, hydrogenase was a molybdo-flavoprotein which acts as a 1-electron acceptor between FAD and cytochrome-c as follows:

$$H_2 \rightarrow \text{flavine-adenine-dinucleotide (FAD)} \rightarrow Mo \rightarrow \text{cytochrome-c}$$

Nicholas[379] on the other hand found that *Azotobacter* and *Clostridium* hydrogenases both reduce ferric iron to ferrous iron and that ferrous iron reduces cytochrome-c non-enzymatically, indicating that iron is involved. He was unable to say whether or not molybdenum was also active in the system. Other evidence also suggests it is an iron-containing enzyme.[417]

In *Clostridium pasteurianum*[362] it has been possible to separate two fractions, one of which contains the hydrogenase system, the other probably containing the nitrogenase. Neither fraction fixes nitrogen alone but they do so in combination. The hydrogenase is contained in what has been termed the hydrogen-donating system (HDS). This fraction is prepared by heating the cell extract under hydrogen at 60°C and then discarding the denatured protein. It contains, in addition to hydrogenase, the phosphoroclastic system, as it can convert pyruvate to acetyl phosphate, carbon dioxide and hydrogen. It thus contains the enzymes necessary for reduction of the molecular nitrogen. The second fraction, termed the nitrogen activating system (NAS), is obtained as a clear amber solution after removal of various other fractions by treatment with protamine sulphate and aged calcium-phosphate gel. This fraction contains only about 5 per cent of the pyruvic acid dehydrogenase activity and has little hydrogenase activity. Evidence has been obtained by a series of ingenious experiments that the NAS probably contains the nitrogenase system and these may be summarized as follows:

(1) When ammonia is added to cell-free extracts nitrogen fixation is inhibited, therefore nitrogenase is either not formed or is inactive. Conversion of pyruvate to acetyl-phosphate, carbon dioxide and hydrogen still continues however. (2) When the HDS from ammonia-grown or nitrogen-fixing cells is added to the NAS from nitrogen-fixing cells fixation occurs, that is, HDS formation is not dependent on the form of nitrogen supplied. (3) When the HDS from ammonia-grown or nitrogen-fixing cells is added to the NAS from ammonia-grown cells there is no fixation, therefore nitrogen-fixing activity in the NAS is inhibited by combined nitrogen. The methods of preparing these fractions do not allow them both to be obtained from the same batch, so that similar components are probably present in both fractions. It is thus difficult to characterize each completely. From this evidence and that obtained by Bulen and his co-workers which showed that a hydrogenase fraction from *Clostridium* supported nitrogen fixation by a nitrogenase preparation from *Azotobacter*,[95] it now seems clear that in micro-organisms the hydrogenase and nitrogenase are two distinct entities, and not part of a single multifunctional enzyme as previously proposed.[594]

Finally one must consider how these two systems, the hydrogenase and nitrogenase, are interrelated. Firstly, pyruvate appears to play a central rôle in the fixation process in *Clostridium* although it has not been shown to be necessary in some organisms. In *Clostridium* the rate of fixation can be governed by the rate of pyruvate oxidation—if the oxidation rate is low, or very high, fixation is sub-optimal. Secondly the phosphoroclastic reaction produces electrons which probably combine ultimately with ferredoxin to give reduced ferredoxin. Thirdly as noted previously, both molecular nitrogen and ammonium-nitrogen inhibit hydrogen evolution in whole cells of anaerobes even in low concentrations. Fourthly it has also been found, for example in cell-free extracts of *Clostridium* that when a hydrogen-acceptor such as methyl viologen is provided, fixation is inhibited.[365] These findings therefore suggest that the hydrogenase and nitrogenase systems may compete for electrons generated, presumably from pyruvate and available as reduced ferredoxin and anything favouring the conversion of electrons to molecular hydrogen results in a shortage of electrons for nitrogen reduction. On this basis the ability of molecular hydrogen to act as a source of electrons for fixation by cell-free extracts in the presence of acetyl phosphate and in the absence of pyruvate can be explained because this reverses the direction of the reaction:

$$\text{reduced ferredoxin} \rightarrow H_2 + \text{ferredoxin}$$

so that reduced Fd is produced and in the presence of an energy source can be used to reduce molecular nitrogen on the nitrogenase.

This could also explain the inhibitory effect of molecular hydrogen on fixation by whole cells, which must contain pyruvate, or in cell-free extracts supplied with pyruvate, for then the electrons made available from molecular hydrogen would compete with those from the phosphoroclastic reaction for ferredoxin. Thus the phosphoroclastic reaction would slow down, and while sufficient electrons would still be available for reduction of the nitrogen, acetyl phosphate also produced in this reaction would be limiting, and fixation perhaps inhibited through lack of energy. These interreactions can be represented thus:

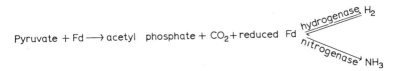

Possible interactions in the nitrogen-fixing process are represented diagrammatically in Fig. 16 (p. 116). Although put forward here as a general scheme, much of it is based on evidence for *Clostridium*, and part of it follows closely a scheme proposed for this organism by Mortenson. As more evidence becomes available it may well have to be modified.[358] It is suggested that in nitrogen-fixing organisms in general pyruvate derived either from photosynthesis or from exogenous carbohydrate via respiration supplies acetyl phosphate for ATP synthesis and that it also supplies electrons for the reduction of nitrogen. These electrons are passed on to an electron carrier which is represented here as ferredoxin although it should be emphasized that ferredoxin has not yet been found in aerobic nitrogen-fixing bacteria such as *Azotobacter*. The electrons from reduced ferredoxin are passed to the nitrogenase system where the nitrogen is

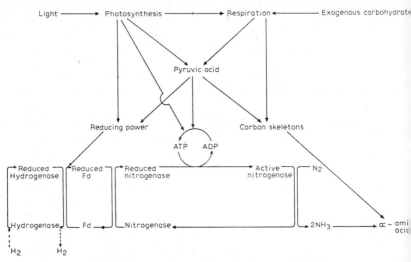

Fig. 16. A tentative scheme for nitrogen fixation.

reduced. Should any reduced ferredoxin not be used up in nitrogen reduction its electrons are passed on to the hydrogenase system and molecular hydrogen is liberated. Pyruvate may also supply a source of carbon skeletons either directly or via α-ketoglutarate. In addition to the pathway via pyruvate direct photoreduction of nitrogen may occur in photosynthetic organisms, and carbon skeletons and energy may also become available by other routes. Finally in *Clostridium*, but not in all organisms, for example *Azotobacter*, molecular hydrogen may act as a reductant.

9 Nitrogen Fixation in the Field

In earlier chapters the structure, physiology and biochemistry of nitrogen-fixing organisms have been discussed. It now remains to consider how much nitrogen these organisms fix in the field, and what their contribution is to the fertility of soils, lakes and seas. Their agricultural importance has attracted attention ever since it became clear that biological nitrogen fixation supplies the major part of combined nitrogen now in circulation, or, to put it another way since it became evident that non-biologically fixed nitrogen accounts for only a small proportion of the total nitrogen requirements of the Earth. For example, it was calculated in 1959 that only about 6 per cent of the total nitrogen required for annual food production of the world was supplied as artificial inorganic fertilizer.[149] Today, as in the days of Boussingault, Hellriegel and Wilfarth, the legumes, as the plants extensively used in agriculture are regarded as the pre-eminent nitrogen fixers of the Earth, but the contributions of the non-legumes, the blue-green algae, and the bacteria may nevertheless all be considerable. In the following pages methods of measuring nitrogen fixation in the field will be briefly discussed and a resumé given of some of the results obtained.

9.2 Measurement of nitrogen fixation under natural conditions

The methods which can be used are dictated by the habitat and the nitrogen-fixing organisms being studied. All have technical difficulties and limitations. The following are mainly used:

1. *Total nitrogen analyses*
This is perhaps the most satisfactory with legumes and involves measuring total nitrogen present in crop plus soil per unit area.

either before and after nodulated plants had been grown, or in two comparable areas, one with and the other without the test crop. With perennial plants such as the nitrogen-fixing non-legumes fixation may be assessed by estimating the total nitrogen present in comparable sites bearing plants of different ages. The following comparative and indirect methods are also used: (a) analyses of total soil nitrogen in the presence and absence of the nitrogen-fixing plant, (b) comparison of crop yield in the presence of the nodulated plant with that in the presence of a known quantity of nitrogen fertilizer, (c) comparison of crop yields or the amounts of nitrogen made available to the soil in the form of leaf litter in areas with plants of different ages or in areas subjected to different treatments, (d) determination of subsequent crop yields, or protein yield of grazing animals in areas where nitrogen-fixing plants had been, or had not been, grown. With free-living organisms it is difficult to measure fixation by the total nitrogen method because sampling errors, the general lack of sensitivity and the fact that a proportion of the nitrogen fixed may be liberated extracellularly and lost by leaching, all lead to errors.

2. *Use of the isotope* ^{15}N

This method has been used to estimate fixation in the field by the nodulated non-leguminous plant *Hippophaë*, the nodules of which retain their nitrogen-fixing capacity for a considerable period after detachment. It involves excavating portions of nodulated roots, detaching these from the plant and immediately exposing them in the field to ^{15}N-labelled molecular nitrogen for a short time. From the following formula:

$$\frac{\text{Atom per cent excess } ^{15}\text{N in nodule}}{\text{Atom per cent excess } ^{15}\text{N in gas mixture}} \times \frac{\text{Total nodule}}{\text{nitrogen}}$$

the nitrogen fixed per nodule sample is calculated, and from a knowledge of the mean nodule nitrogen per unit volume of soil the total quantity of nitrogen fixed can be determined. Disadvantages of this method are that during exposure the nodules are no longer in their natural environment, and that there may be a fall-off in their nitrogen-fixing activity with time. However, if exposure periods are short, little error is likely to be introduced, although the results obtained must be regarded as minimal values. The ^{15}N method is most suitable for experiments with free-living micro-organisms, for whole nitrogen-fixing units can be easily enclosed. So far it has been used to obtain measures of fixation in soils,[143] in fresh-water[159,162] and in marine habitats.[496-7] The older method, that of measuring the volume of molecular nitrogen which disappears from a sealed system containing the test sample, has also been employed to measure algal nitrogen fixation in rice paddy fields,[142] but it has numerous technical difficulties and is now rarely used.

9.3 The legumes

The importance of these plants in relation to soil fertility depends on whether or not they fix atmospheric nitrogen. To do this they must be effectively nodulated and it appears that many wild legumes are, for they rapidly colonize nitrogen-deficient habitats, for example, abandoned and nutritionally exhausted arable lands, gravel wastes and newly cleared areas. In the west of Scotland approximately 95 per cent of the rhizobia strains isolated from the nodules of the wild legume *Ulex europaeus* (gorse) are effective.[331] The importance of having appropriate rhizobia in the soil is seen particularly when cultivated legumes are introduced into areas from which they are normally absent, or into freshly reclaimed land, or areas devastated by fire etc.,[7] for then nodulation fails to occur due to lack of effective rhizobia. This has led to the present day practice of introducing both the legume and appropriate rhizobia simultaneously. By this method effective rhizobial strains for specific plants are isolated on bacteriological media, built up into commercial quantities, and then made available to the farmer, mixed with fine peat or soil, or in agar or liquid culture. The rhizobia and legume seed may be added to the ground separately or the seed may be coated with the rhizobial supplement before sowing. To increase the chances of survival and growth, and thus ultimately nodulation, several different strains may be included in each inoculum. A most interesting account of the early studies using pure rhizobia as inocula, has been given in the monograph by Fred, Baldwin and McCoy.[201] Providing effective nodules are present and other conditions for growth are satisfactory nitrogen fixation should occur, for the levels of combined nitrogen in the soil are seldom likely to be so high as to inhibit fixation completely.

Certain elements may be limiting in some soils. For example, molybdenum may be present in sub-optimal quantities.[19] In such areas small amounts of molybdenum added either to the soil or as a foliar spray, markedly improve growth and fixation, additions of as little as 1 oz molybdenum per acre having spectacular results in some Australian soils.[19] In other areas, such as parts of Britain characterized by acid soils, molybdenum, although present in ample quantity, may be largely unavailable because of the low pH. In acid soils molybdenum deficiency can often be overcome by liming the soil to increase the pH. Additions of cobalt may similarly stimulate fixation is some areas, for example, in Australian soils increases in the yield of lucerne ranging from 29–77 per cent have been obtained and the nitrogen fixed per unit weight of nodules markedly increased on the addition of cobalt.[425] There is little doubt that other fertilizers such as phosphate also increase the amounts of nitrogen fixed by increasing overall plant growth. The data summarized in Table 9 provide information on the amounts of nitrogen fixed by some

TABLE 9. Average amounts of nitrogen
fixed by various legume crops

Legume	Nitrogen fixed (lb per acre per year)
Red clover	103
Sweet clover	93
White clover	133
Lucerne	158
Soya bean	84
Mixed legumes	112

of the commoner leguminous crops. These values are means obtained from over fifty reports scattered throughout the literature. Most of the references are available in other reviews.[93,201,252] An average value is probably in the range of 100–200 lb per acre per year, although large variations must obviously occur and values as high as 733 lb per acre per year have been obtained.[478]

In agriculture, legumes are grown principally as a source of combined nitrogen for non-nitrogen-fixing crops, as a food source for grazing animals, and for human consumption. Their widespread use in pastures is perhaps exemplified by the fact that in Germany legumes account for approximately 8–10 per cent of the total plant cover of grassland regions.[565] These legumes not only increase soil fertility but may be richer than grasses in high quality protein (Table 10) and in certain vita-

TABLE 10. Comparison of percentage protein content of certain legumes and grasses (ref. 565)

Species	Crude protein per plant (per cent)
Legumes	
Medicago tribuloides	17·2
Trifolium subterraneum	12·0
Trifolium repens	12·3
Mean	13·8
Grasses	
Lolium perenne	5·5
Phalaris tuberosa	4·9
Dactylis glomerata	5·4
Mean	5·3

mins, calcium and phosphorus.[565] The commonest pasture legume in Britain is white clover (*Trifolium repens*) but *Medicago sativa* (lucerne or alfalfa) is frequently used in the United States and in Australia[565] and was used by Boussingault as early as 1844 when he recorded an annual gain in nitrogen of 130 lb per acre per year.[87] Sometimes early and late strains are planted simultaneously to prolong the nitrogen-fixing activity of the crop. This method provides a more even supply of fixed nitrogen to a crop than would be available from artificial nitrogen fertilizer which is all added at once.

There is little doubt that the contribution of fixed nitrogen would probably be greater if the legumes were grown in pure stands but this is seldom carried out for the crop would be so rich in nitrogen that there would be a shortage of carbohydrate for the grazing animal. Detrimental effects on cattle feeding on pure legume pastures have been noted under certain conditions.

Furthermore it is a difficult matter in practice to achieve a pure legume pasture for the high nitrogen content encourages the growth of weeds. It is thus more desirable to introduce along with the legume a suitable grass which will assimilate the excess nitrogen and increase the carbohydrate status of the overall crop. By growing a mixed pasture of this type it is generally possible to achieve a higher total crop yield (though not necessarily greater total fixation) than if the legume had been grown alone. In mixed pastures the nitrogen becomes available to the grass mainly as animal excreta although under conditions such as those pertaining in pastoral regions, that is, shading and defoliation of the legumes, nodule shedding is often stimulated and as much as 71 lb per acre per year may be released into the soil in this way.[114] In the tropics legumes and grasses are rarely grown intermixed because the latter are on the whole tall plants which shade the legume excessively. In such instances the grasses and legumes may be grown in alternate rows.[166]

While the pastoral or dairy farmer makes widespread use of the legume, the arable farmer seldom uses it solely to increase soil fertility. The older method was to introduce into the rotation a legume which was ploughed into the soil as green manure. There is no doubt that this procedure increases the nitrogen status of the soil as can be seen from Table 11 where the least beneficial legume (Chilean alfalfa) provided nitrogen equivalent to an application of approximately 96 lb per acre of ammonium nitrate and the most beneficial (Hairy vetch) to an application of approximately 142 lb per acre.[304a] Few farmers, however, can afford to allow their land to lie for a complete year without showing any financial return and this method is not used very often in modern agricultural practice. Instead, one of the three following methods is commonly employed: (1) Growing the legume out of season for use as a green manure, (2) introducing a legume/grass pasture into the rotation, or (3) introducing a legume crop which can be harvested and used as hay or as a grain crop.

The use of winter legumes as a green manure and as a cover crop is becoming increasingly popular and has several advantages in countries such as Britain where the winter is not too severe.[565] First, soil nitrogen is being increased when the ground would otherwise have remained fallow. Secondly, it provides a source of winter grazing. Thirdly, it prevents erosion. Winter green manures are also frequently used in maize and cotton fields in the United States but in some areas they provide no real advantage if the crop is harvested and indeed may deplete

TABLE 11. The effect of legume green manure on subsequent nitrogen yield of barley (ref. 304a)

Legume	Legume N added to soil in 1952 (lbs per acre)	Total N in barley grain and straw in 1953 (lbs per acre)
Alfalfa (lucerne)		
Arizona common	76	51·4
Chilean	70	37·1
Argentine	81	53·1
African	87	43·9
Ladak	83	43·8
Ranger	69	39·4
Sweet clover		
Madrid	181	41·2
Hubam	52	44·4
Vetch		
Madison	96	53·4
Hairy	79	54·9
Ammonium nitrate (120 lb per acre)	—	46·3
No treatment	—	31·0

the soil. However when winter crops are ploughed into the soil gains of the order of 30–60 lb per acre have been achieved. In the tropics and sub-tropics the technique of growing legumes as a cover crop is frequently employed, for example in tea plantations it is common to grow a legume crop and the tea bushes in alternate rows.[166] This procedure not only increases soil fertility but cuts down water loss and prevents erosion.

The second possibility is to introduce into the rotation a legume/grass mixture which is used for grazing. This is probably the most satisfactory method of all, for it provides food for the grazing animal and yet a high proportion of the nitrogen fixed is returned to the soil as animal excreta. The third possibility is to introduce a legume of commercial value into the rotation.

Lucerne is commonly used in this connexion, for example in the United States in 1949 approximately 17 million tons of lucerne were cut as hay.[565] An alternative possibility is to grow a mixed crop of legumes and cereals and to harvest this for silage. The legumes popularly used in silage are the clovers, peas, and lupins. In Britain silage provides a protein-rich supplement for dairy cattle. In America it is fed to pigs and poultry, and is used to prevent nutrient deficiencies in grazing animals.[565] These methods, although providing an annual income for the farmer, result in a much smaller return of fixed nitrogen to the soil than would have been achieved by a summer green manure and, as can be seen from Table 12, decreases in total soil nitrogen may

TABLE 12. The effect of various leguminous crops on subsequent crop yield and nitrogen status of the soil (ref. 327)

| | Nitrogen harvested | | Gain or Loss of N in soil per rotation (lb per acre) | Yield of cereal grain (cwt per acre) |
	Leguminous crop (lb per acre)	Cereal crop (lb per acre)		
Lucerne	299	66	121	23·2
Clover	125	51	114	19·4
Sweet clover	169	51	84	18·9
Soya beans	176	29	−8	11·8
Field beans	103	25	−20	10·6
Cereal every year	—	22	−10	8·7

actually result. This is because a high proportion of the nitrogen fixed occurs in the aerial part of the plant, less than 20–30 per cent generally remaining in the root system (Table 13). When a grain crop such as peas or soya beans is used in the rotation the return to the soil is even smaller for the seeds are very rich in

TABLE 13. The distribution of nitrogen in nodulated legumes (ref. 281)

| Species | Percentage of total plant nitrogen | | |
	Tops	Roots	Nodules
Medicago sativa	50–66	29–43	4·5–12·5
Medicago tribuloides	80–82	13–15	3·4– 7·2
Trifolium subterraneum	69–85	11–21	3·6–12·6
Trifolium repens	81–84	11–14	3·5– 4·4

nitrogen. The mean contribution of fixed nitrogen to the soil from grain crops is probably in the region of 30–60 lb per acre, although as much as 200 lb per acre has been recorded.[607] Generally the price of the harvested crop offsets the disadvantages of small gains in soil nitrogen.

9.4 The non-legumes

The nitrogen-fixing non-legumes, being woody perennials, are of little agricultural importance. They have been used occasionally in forestry to build up the nitrogen status of the soil and are planted in certain barren areas presumably for the same reason, for example *Myrica* is planted on peat on the west coast of Scotland[372] and *Alnus* is used in certain areas of south-east Asia.[301,573] They are most important in increasing the nitrogen status of their natural habitats.

As with the legumes their importance depends on whether they are fixing nitrogen—thus nodules must be present. As mentioned previously, field material of the three native British genera, *Alnus*, *Myrica* and *Hippophaë*, is invariably abundantly nodulated. For example the data obtained by Stewart and Pearson[499] for *Hippophaë* growing on a sand dune system are summarized in Table 14 and show: First, all plants bore nodules

TABLE 14. Growth and nodulation of *Hippophaë rhamnoides* in the field (ref. 499)

Mean age of plants (years)	3	11	13	16
1. Nodule number per m² of soil surface	98	370	313	22
2. Total plant weight per m² of soil surface (gm)	1053	1997	4317	13929
3. Total nodule weight per m² of soil surface (gm)	2·5	39·0	64·2	2·7
4. Nodule weight as per cent of total plant weight	0·24	1·95	1·49	0·02
5. Per cent nitrogen content of roots + shoots	0·61	0·64	0·66	0·54
6. Per cent nitrogen content of nodules	1·5	1·2	1·3	1·0

indicating the widespread distribution of the endophyte and nodule numbers increased with age except on very old plants where presumably shading and overcrowding inhibited fresh nodulation (line 1). Secondly, nodule weight as a percentage of total plant weight also decreased on old plants (lines 2–4). Thirdly, the percentage nitrogen content of the nodules was higher than that of the remainder of the plant indicating that they fixed nitrogen (lines 5 and 6). As the endophytes of non-legumes cannot readily be isolated, the degree of nodulation of field material provides an indication of the distribution of the endophyte in the soil; the other way of finding this out is to plant uninoculated seedlings in soils from various areas and to determine the number of nodules formed. Quispel has used this method to demonstrate multiplication of the *Alnus* endophyte within a particular soil.[435]

Greenhouse experiments show that there should be no difficulty in growing mature trees or bushes in the complete absence of combined nitrogen and that the levels of combined nitrogen in the field are unlikely to inhibit nodulation and fixation to any great extent[493,498] particularly as the inorganic nitrogen in the soil is lowest during the months when rapid growth and fixation occur.[499] Bond, in 1956, was one of the first to study fixation by non-legumes in the field, when by using ^{15}N-labelled nitrogen he showed that excavated alder nodules still attached to the tree assimilated the heavy isotope.[73] Other workers have shown fixation by detached field nodules of the following genera: *Alnus, Comptonia, Discaria* (see 3.2), *Coriaria*[242] and *Hippophaë*.[499] As an example of the quantitative data we may consider as typical some of those available for the two temperate genera *Alnus* and *Hippophaë*, and for *Casuarina*, a tropical genus.

Some of the most interesting data for *Alnus* have been obtained by Crocker and Major[131] who found *Alnus crispa* and *Shepherdia* among the most vigorous early colonizers of recently deglaciated areas in Alaska. They suggested a nitrogen-fixing function for *Alnus*, being unaware that its nitrogen-fixing function had long been known, and calculated that leaf fall contributed approximately 55 lb nitrogen per acre per year to the soil. This increase in soil nitrogen resulted in the establishment of sitka spruce which ultimately suppressed alder and caused a decrease in soil nitrogen. The importance of *Alnus* trees in these areas has been emphasized by Lawrence[309] who records how they 'not only grow rapidly themselves but also stimulate to vigorous erect growth adjacent shrubs and trees which were previously grovelling as semi-prostrate individuals'. For example plants associated with *Alnus* were 22·5 times greater in weight, than those in comparable areas without *Alnus*. Other workers have calculated that *Alnus glutinosa* trees, over a period of eight years, fix approximately 200 lb nitrogen per acre per year[551] and that in thirty year-old *Alnus* stands intermixed with Douglas Fir approximately 36 lb nitrogen per acre per year are fixed.[508] *Alnus* trees growing around the margins of certain lakes may also provide a nitrogen supplement in the form of leaf litter.[224]

The best evidence for *Casuarina* has been obtained by Dommergues,[153] who calculated from data for two areas, one with, and the other without *Casuarina*, that it fixed 52 lb per acre per year over a thirteen year period. Finally, studies on *Hippophaë* by Stewart and Pearson[499] using the ^{15}N method described in 9.2 show that in the field this plant fixes large quantities of nitrogen. The data summarized in Table 15 show that the

TABLE 15. Nitrogen fixation by *Hippophaë rhamnoides* in the field (ref. 499)

Mean age of plant (years)	3	11	13	16
Mean atom per cent excess ^{15}N in nodules* after 2 hours exposure	0·139	0·108	0·083	0·062
Total nodule nitrogen per m² (mg)	38	468	835	27
Nitrogen fixed per m² per 2 hour period (mg)	0·30	2·86	3·93	0·10
Nitrogen fixed (lb per acre per year)	4·76	45·43	62·44	1·58

* Atom per cent excess ^{15}N in gas mixture = 17·648.

youngest nodules were most active in fixation but that because of the greater total nodule weight, maximum fixation occurs in trees thirteen years old. These fix at least 62 lb per acre per season assuming that, as in *Almus*,[490] fixation occurs in Britain during a four-month summer season. The youngest and oldest plants fix comparatively little nitrogen because of the few nodules present. It should be re-emphasized that because of the limitations of this method these values must be taken as minimal values and that the amounts of nitrogen fixed by nodules still attached to the plant may be somewhat higher.

Quantitative data for certain non-legumes are summarized in Table 16 and, as can be seen, a conservative estimate of the amounts of nitrogen fixed is of the order of 50–100 lb per acre per year, most of which probably becomes available to the soil as leaf litter.

TABLE 16. Quantities of nitrogen fixed by non-leguminous nitrogen-fixing organisms

Group	Species or habitat	Mean nitrogen fixed (lb per acre per year)	References
Nodulated non-legumes	Alnus crispa	55	131
	Alnus crispa	148	309
	Alnus glutinosa	200	551
	Casuarina equisetifolia	52	153
	Myrica gale	8	70
	Hippophaë rhamnoides (13 years old)	62	499
Blue-green algae	In arid Australian soils	3	510
	In Indian paddy fields	>13	426
	In Indian paddy fields	30	142
	Aulosira fertilissima in Indian paddy fields	48	475
	Cylindrospermum licheniforme in Indian paddy fields	80	475
Free-living soil micro-organisms (?)	Under Pinus	32	488
	Under Pinus	56	150
	Under wheat	22	478
	Under wheat	38	570
	Under mustard	40	121
	Tropical bare soil	110	272
	Under Eleusine coracana	100–130	349
	Under regenerated African bush	640	272

9.5 The blue-green algae

Unlike the symbiotic nitrogen-fixing plants, the blue-green algae are generally inconspicuous organisms, but despite this they make a valuable contribution to the fertility of many environments. As noted previously, only genera which possess heterocysts have so far been shown conclusively to fix nitrogen.

This is a valuable characteristic, for the nitrogen-fixing potential of a particular habitat can be assessed simply by determining the abundance of heterocystous algae. Whether fixation actually occurs depends on the environmental conditions pertaining at a particular time. Little work has been done on the availability of nutrients for blue-green algae in the field but there is evidence that certain nutrients may on occasion be limiting, for example in Indian rice paddy fields fixation can be stimulated by adding phosphate and molybdate.[142]

Of the various physical conditions governing fixation, the presence or absence of light is perhaps the most important. A profile through any soil will show the blue-green algae to be almost entirely restricted to the surface layers, as would be expected of primarily photosynthetic organisms. This can be seen clearly in Fig. 17 in which algal abundance and the amount of nitrogen fixed at various depths in an area of sand-dune slack are plotted, and from which it is evident that both the algae and the ability to fix nitrogen are almost entirely

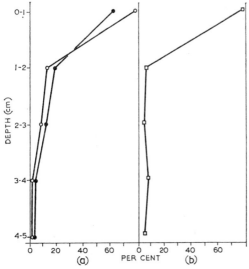

FIG. 17. Blue-green algae and nitrogen fixation in a dune-slack region. (a) Relative abundance of total (●—●) and heterocystous (○—○) blue-green algae with depth. (b) Relative nitrogen fixation at various depths. (after ref. 496)

restricted to the surface centimetre of soil.[496] Also, it has been shown that fixation in surface samples is several times higher in the light than in the dark.[496] Their ability to withstand temperature extremes may explain the abundance of blue-green algae in winter in certain temperate regions such as salt marshes, and is probably one reason why these organisms comprise an important part of the vegetation of the Antarctic, for even at extremes of temperature which inhibit fixation the algae remain alive and are capable of fixing nitrogen again immediately the temperature rises. Desiccation, although unimportant in temperate regions, except during the summer months, is probably the most important factor affecting fixation in the tropics. In Indian rice paddy fields abundant algal growth occurs only during, and for a relatively short time after, the monsoon.[475] Hydrogen-ion concentration is unlikely to be a factor markedly inhibiting nitrogen fixation except in acid soils.

When one comes to consider the quantitative data one of the first things that becomes obvious is that relatively few data are available, even although so many nitrogen-fixing species are now known. Several workers have estimated, on the basis of pure culture studies in the laboratory, the amounts of nitrogen which blue-green algae may fix in terms of pounds per acre per year, but the value of such calculations is doubtful. The areas which have been studied most are the following: (1) rice paddy fields, (2) regions where algae are primary colonizers, (3) marine habitats, and (4) lakes. Each of these will be briefly considered and some of the quantitative data available are summarized in Table 16 (p. 128). These are largely values for fixation per paddy crop rather than for amounts of nitrogen accumulated over a twelve-month period.

1. *Nitrogen fixation in rice fields*

Any factor affecting the growth of the rice crop in south-east Asia affects the nutrition of almost half the world's population. In this connexion the blue-green algae are important for it is probable that they have been the major contributors of fixed nitrogen for the rice plant in many tropical soils throughout the ages. Within recent years efforts have been made to determine the quantities of nitrogen which they fix, and to develop methods whereby their beneficial effect can be employed to greater advantage.

During the rainy season there is a profuse growth in most paddy fields of species of many nitrogen-fixing genera including *Anabaena, Aulosira, Calothrix, Cylindrospermum, Nostoc* and *Tolypothrix*.[475] The data of De and Mandal[142] give an idea of the amounts of nitrogen fixed. They found that over a 6-week period 13·8–44·4 lb nitrogen per acre were fixed, higher values (up to 70·8 lb per acre) being achieved when fertilizers were added and that the total nitrogen fixed may be up to 20 per cent greater in the presence of a crop than in its absence. This is presumably due to the increased supply of carbon dioxide made available by respiration of the root systems of the rice plants, or to a shading effect of the rice crop. It may be noted that before the nitrogen-fixing capacity of blue-green algae was established it was considered that the better growth of rice plants in the presence of blue-green algae was due to the additional oxygen supply made available to the roots as a result of algal photosynthesis.[91]

The possibility of using blue-green algae as a green manure in paddy fields on a commercial scale was explored by the Japanese worker Watanabe who, from over eight hundred soil samples collected from various parts of south-east Asia, isolated many blue-green algae, four of which fixed nitrogen in pure culture: *Tolypothrix tenuis, Calothrix brevissima, Anabaenopsis* sp. and *Nostoc* sp.[561] In laboratory culture experiments *Tolypothrix* proved to be the most suitable for further studies—it was the most rapid nitrogen-fixing species and it also improved the growth of rice plants in nitrogen-free medium. Watanabe then devised methods for mass-culturing and handling the alga, the most suitable of which was to grow the organism on moist sterilized porous gravel in which form it could be stored for up to three years in air-tight bags without loss of activity. Investigations were carried out at eleven experimental stations in various parts of Japan, quantities of 1–5 lb dry weight of alga per acre per year being applied near the time of bedding out the young rice plants. Although various difficulties, such as the consumption of the alga by daphnids, the treated fields showed gains in rice yield of over 20 per cent per annum both in areas of high and low nitrogen status.[561] It has been calculated that fertilization using *Tolypothrix* is equivalent to applying approximately 26 lb of ammonium sulphate per acre. More recently experiments have been carried out on mass culturing the alga in large outdoor open tanks heated to 30°C with hot spring water, and using natural methane gas as a source of carbon dioxide.[562] It seems possible that the commercial application of nitrogen-fixing blue-green algae may assume more importance in years to come although a considerable reduction in the cost of mass culturing the algae will have to be achieved before it can compete economically with artificial inorganic fertilizer.

2. *Blue-green algae as primary colonizers*

The importance of blue-green algae in rice fields has led to investigations into methods of increasing their contribution of fixed nitrogen in this situation. In certain other habitats these organisms make a valuable contribution of fixed nitrogen without any stimulatory treatment whatsoever. For example, on bare rocks in Soviet mountain ranges blue-green algae are reported to fix as much as 220 lb nitrogen per acre per 6-month period, a proportion of which must ultimately contribute to the nitrogen status of the valleys below.[303] In Indian mountains and hills the known nitrogen-fixing genera *Stigonema* and *Nostoc* are common on bare rock surfaces, while *Calothrix*, *Fischerella* and *Tolypothrix* are also recorded, but the quantities of nitrogen fixed have not been calculated.[475]

The rapidity with which blue-green algae colonize newly exposed substrata is perhaps best seen in the much quoted example—the abundance of these organisms on the volcanic island of Krakatau, three years after its formation in 1885.[524] It has been suggested that the ferns which were the most abundant vascular plants present, germinated only because of the suitable substratum afforded by the gelatinous growth of blue-green algae, which included *Tolypothrix* and *Anabaena* species. Blue-green algae are considered important primary colonizers in both hot and cold desert regions. The absolute quantities of nitrogen fixed may not be high but nevertheless may be of crucial importance in these inhospitable habitats where there is an acute shortage of combined nitrogen. In arid

Australian soils fixation by blue-green algae has been calculated as approximately 3 lb per acre per year.[510] In desert
areas of North America blue-green algae are widespreadly
distributed and in the Sonoran desert[115] and in Death Valley,
California[163] *Nostoc* and *Anabaena* respectively are two of the
most abundant algae recorded. Evidence of algal nitrogen
fixation in such desert areas has been obtained.[116] Much
of the recent work on desert algae in relation to soil fertility
has been reviewed by Shields and Durrell.[466] In the Antarctic
the nitrogen-fixing genus *Nostoc* is the chief component of 'algal
peat' which forms layers 4–6 inches deep in certain regions.[265]

3. *Nitrogen fixation in marine habitats*

Although it is known that the legumes and non-legumes are
responsible for a high proportion of the nitrogen annually fixed
in terrestrial habitats the sources of combined nitrogen in the
sea are still uncertain. Obviously a proportion is derived from
run-off from land, and from rain, but it is also known that
nitrogen-fixing marine micro-organisms, including blue-green
algae, occur.

Among the planktonic blue-green algae there is evidence that
fixation is associated with species of the genus *Trichodesmium*.
These are red pigmented forms which occur abundantly at certain times of the year in parts of the Sargasso Sea, the Arabian
Sea and Indian Ocean.[160] Freshly collected samples rapidly
incorporate ^{15}N-labelled molecular nitrogen but fixation has yet
to be established in pure cultures of the algae. Another planktonic form is a species of *Nostoc*, which occurs abundantly down
to depths of 600 metres in the Mediterranean and Arabian
Sea at certain times of the year.[59] This alga which presumably grows heterotrophically at such depths has not been tested
for nitrogen fixation but as all *Nostoc* species tested for fixation to
date do so, it is likely that this one does too.

In temperate regions blue-green algae are abundant in the
upper littoral and supralittoral fringe of the seashore and in salt
marsh regions.[203] The species for which there is evidence of fixation belong to the genera *Anabaena*, *Calothrix*, *Nodularia*, *Nostoc*
and *Scytonema*.[496] Of these *Calothrix* is the dominant intertidal
epilithic blue-green alga on temperate shores.[202–3] Potential

nitrogen-fixing genera represent approximately 33 per cent and 90 per cent of the total blue-green algae present at certain times of the year in a developing salt marsh[500] and in a supra-littoral rocky shore[496] region respectively. This compares with a value of 25 per cent for a fresh-water habitat.[572]

Using the ^{15}N technique Stewart has shown both in a sand dune slack dominated by gelatinous Myxophyceae such as *Nostoc* and *Anabaena*, and in an epilithic habitat dominated by *Calothrix* that there was little or no nitrogen fixation in February and January respectively although the algae were abundant, but that fixation increased markedly in the spring and in April and May values of 7·1 lb per acre per month and 4·6 lb per acre per month were obtained for the dune slack and epilithic floras respectively.[496-7] In the former area, as much as 18·2 lb per acre per month were fixed in areas with a particularly rich algal cover, a value comparable to that obtained in some Indian paddy fields. More data has to be accumulated on the amounts of nitrogen fixed in such habitats, but it does seem certain that blue-green algae provide an important source of combined nitrogen for surrounding organisms.

4. *Nitrogen fixation in lakes*

Blue-green algae occur abundantly at certain times of the year in eutrophic lakes, where they may form water-blooms. Certain of the common bloom-formers, for example *Microcystis aeruginosa*, do not fix nitrogen, but others, such as *Anabaena flos-aquae*[227] and *Anabaenopsis circularis*,[475] as well as species from lakes and streams: *Nostoc muscorum*, *Nostoc* sp., and *Calothrix parietina*,[572] do so in pure culture. In addition other species of *Anabaena* and *Anabaenopsis*, as well as species of *Gloeotrichia*[193] and *Nodularia*[491, 496] probably do likewise.

The suggestion that algal nitrogen fixation in lakes may be important was made by Hutchinson on the basis of the direct correlation between gains in total nitrogen in lakes and the abundance of *Anabaena*.[271] This suggestion has recently been supported by ^{15}N data which show that the abundance of *Anabaena*, the amounts of nitrogen fixed, and the quantities of nitrogen present in lakes can all be fairly directly correlated. For example, data obtained for Sanctuary Lake, Pennsylvania, and reproduced in Fig. 18 show that *Anabaena* is present from late April until mid-November, is abundant in August, September and early October and reaches maxima in August and early October.[159] Fixation begins to increase markedly in late July when the quantities of inorganic nitrogen are at a minimum

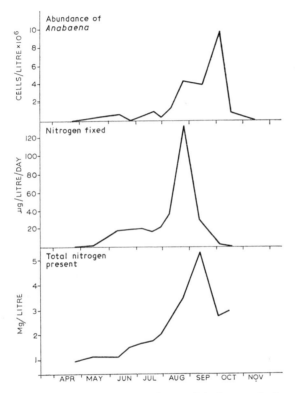

Fig. 18. Correlation between abundance of *Anabaena* and nitrogen fixation in a eutrophic lake (after ref. 159).

(ammonium and nitrate-nitrogen data are not shown in Fig. 18) and at this stage the nitrogen-fixing blue-green algae are probably at a competitive advantage. Total nitrogen in the lake increases to a maximum about the middle of September. Other factors which suggest that blue-green algae are responsible for fixation is that the process is largely light dependent, and also it is unlikely that sufficient readily oxidizable carbo-hydrate is available to allow heterotrophic nitrogen fixation to occur on such a scale. Data obtained by the Russian worker Kusnezow support the suggestion that fixation in lakes is largely algal in origin.[306] He found that during the summer season in a Russian lake total fixation by *Anabaena* was approxi-mately 90,000 times greater than fixation by *Azotobacter*. As can be seen from Fig. 18 quantities of up to 126 μg. nitrogen per litre per day are fixed during the period of maximum fixation.

9.6 Bacterial nitrogen fixation

The contribution of bacterial nitrogen fixation to soil fertility has received relatively little attention, presumably because for almost fifty years *Azotobacter* and *Clostridium* were the only gener-ally accepted nitrogen-fixing species, and yet it was evident that they were unlikely to be important in relation to soil fertility. An assessment of their abundance in soils made it clear that they were seldom present in sufficient quantity to be important contributors of combined nitrogen. For example *Azotobacter* though most abundant in agricultural soils is present in numbers of less than 200 cells per gram of Rothamsted soils,[452] and this is probably about an average number for temperate agricultural soils. Even lower counts have been obtained in other soils. In Denmark less than 100 cells were present per gram of soil in 73 per cent of the numerous soils examined by Jensen.[278] It may be noted that inoculation of the seeds of various agricultural crops with *Azotobacter* has been carried out particularly by Russian workers and there are claims that such inocula increase crop yield. For example, *Azotobacter* has been claimed to increase the yield of oats by 16–21 per cent,[530] while *Beijerinckia* increased the growth of rice by 55 per cent.[152] Other workers however have failed to demonstrate a beneficial effect and it may be that specially selected *Azotobacter* strains are necessary for improved growth. It has also been suggested that *Azotobacter* stimulates growth not by fixing nitrogen but by producing fungal inhibit-ors and growth substances.[346] Secondly as can be seen from Table 5 (p. 72) the efficiency of heterotrophic nitrogen-fixing bacteria (in terms of nitrogen fixed per unit weight of carbohydrate consumed) is not high and is dependent on an adequate carbohydrate supply. As most habitats rich in carbohydrates are generally rich in combined nitrogen too, fixation may be inhibited by the levels of combined nitrogen present. The carbohydrate supply will not of course be a factor limiting fixation by the photosynthetic bacteria or blue-green algae, although the former group, because of their restricted occurrence, are not likely to be important contributors of fixed nitrogen.

Despite these limitations it has become evident since about 1955 that species of many bacterial genera such as *Bacillus*, *Beijerinckia* and *Pseudomonas* fix nitrogen (see Table 5, p. 72) and that these may be of widespread distribution in Nature. Other nitrogen-fixing heterotrophs have, no doubt, still to be discovered. The importance of bacterial nitrogen fixation in the soil is supported by various evidence of gains in combined nitrogen in soils where symbiotic plants are absent: for example, of gains in total nitrogen by wheat crops harvested year after year from the same soil without nitrogen fertilizer being added;[157, 197] of gains of 50 lb per acre per year in soils under rye grass;[409a] and of the nitrogen status of orchards remaining steady for twenty-eight years.[429] Many such results have been noted and some are listed in Table 16 (p. 128). These gains cannot be from nitrogen brought down in rain, for although the contribution from rain must vary, it is generally of the order of 4–10 lb per acre per year[225] or even less.[158] Also some of this must be lost from the soil by leaching and by denitrification. Neither can gains from rain explain why certain soils increase their levels of combined nitrogen when non-nitrogenous fertilizer is added. In 1955 Allison[13] pointed out that in general there was more combined nitrogen being lost from the soil than was added to it by the sources of combined nitrogen then known. It now seems possible that non-symbiotic nitrogen fixation was then underestimated and the time has come therefore when a careful reassessment of the contribution of microbial nitrogen-fixers to soil fertility should be made in the field, using the ^{15}N technique.

References

The pages on which references are cited are indicated thus (67).

1   ABBAYES, H. des (1951). *Encycloped. Biol.*, **41**. Paris: Lechevalier. (67)
2   ABEL, K. (1963). *Phytochemistry*, **2**, 429. (20–1, 35)
3   —, and BAUER, N. (1962). *Arch. Biochem. Biophys.*, **99**, 8. (20)
4   —, —, and SPENCE, J. T. (1963). *Arch. Biochem. Biophys.*, **100**, 338. (20)
5   ALDRICH-BLAKE, R. N. (1932). *Oxf. For. Mem.* No. **14**. (2)
6   ALLEN, E. K., and ALLEN, O. N. (1949). *Proc. Soil Sci. Soc. Amer.*, **14**, 179. (37)
6a —, — (1950). *Bact. Revs.* **14**, 273. (25)
7   —, — (1958). *Encycloped. Plant Physiol.*, **8**, 48. Berlin: Springer-Verlag (6, 11, 25, 33, 37, 119)
8   —, —, and KLEBESADEL, L. J. (1964). *Proc. Alaskan Sci. Conf.*, No. **14**, p. 54. (37)
9   ALLEN, M. B. (1952). *Arch. Mikrobiol.*, **17**, 34. (58, 61–2)
10 — (1956). *Sci. Monthly*, **83**, 100. (58, 95)
11 — (1963). *Symp. Marine Microbiol.*, ed. C. H. Oppenheimer, p. 85. Springfield, Ill.: Thomas. (62, 83)
12 —, and ARNON, D. I. (1955). *Plant Physiol.*, **30**, 366. (60–1)
13 ALLISON, F. E. (1955). *Adv. Agron.*, **7**, 213. (5, 137)
14 —, and HOOVER, S. R. (1935). *Trans. 3rd Int. Congr. Soil Sci.*, **1**, 145. (61–2, 85)
15 —, and LUDWIG, C. A. (1934). *Soil Sci.*, **37**, 431. (41–2)
16 —, —, HOOVER, S. R., and MINOR, F. W. (1940). *Bot. Gaz.*, **101**, 513. (55)
17 —, and MORRIS, H. J. (1930). *Science*, **71**, 221. (62)
18 ALLOS, H. F. and BARTHOLOMEW, W. V. (1955). *Proc. Soil Sci. Soc. Amer.*, **19**, 182. (40)
19 ANDERSON, A. J. (1956). *Inorganic nitrogen metabolism*, ed. W. D. McElroy and B. Glass, p. 3. Baltimore: Johns Hopkins Press. (120)
20 ANDERSON, G. R. (1955). *J. Bacter.*, **70**, 129 (76)
21 APPLEBY, C. A. (1961). *Biochim. Biophys. Acta*, **60**, 226 (55)
22 APRISON, M. H., MAGEE, W. E. and BURRIS, R. H. (1954). *J. biol. Chem.*, **208**, 29. (13)
23 ARNON, D. I. (1958). *Trace elements.* New York: Academic Press. (89)
24 —, LOSADA, M., NOZAKI, M. and TAGAWA, K. (1960a). *Biochem. J.*, **77**, 23P. (6)
25 —, —, —, — (1960b). *Nature, Lond.*, **190**, 601. (6, 75, 79, 86, 106–7)

26 ATWATER, W. O. (1885). *Amer. Chem. J.*, **6**, 365. (*1*)

27 AZIM, M. A. and ROBERTS, E. R. (1955). *Biochim. Biophys. Acta*, **18**, 363. (*94*)

28 —, — (1956*a*). *Biochim. Biophys. Acta*, **21**, 562. (*99*)

29 —, — (1956*b*). *Biochim. Biophys. Acta*, **21**, 308. (*95*)

30 BACH, A., JERMOLJEVA, Z. and STEPANJAN, M. (1934). *Comp. rend. Acad. Sci., U.R.S.S.*, **1**, 22. (*78*)

31 BACH, M. K. (1956). *Inorganic nitrogen metabolism*, ed. W. D. McElroy and B. Glass, p. 370. Baltimore: Johns Hopkins Press. (*77*)

32 — (1957). *Biochim. Biophys. Acta*, **26**, 104. (*99, 104*)

33 —, MAGEE, W. E. and BURRIS, R. H. (1958). *Plant Physiol.*, **33**, 118. (*13, 42*)

34 BACHOFEN, R., BUCHANAN, B. B. and ARNON, D. I. (1964). *Proc. Nat. Acad. Sci., U.S.A.*, **51**, 690. (*91*)

35 BARRIOS, S., RAGGIO, N. and RAGGIO, M. (1963). *Plant Physiol.*, **38**, 171. (*43, 48*)

36 BARTHEL, C. (1932). *Proc. Intern. Congr. Soil Sci., 2nd Congr. Leningrad 1930*, **3**, 72. (*23*)

37 BAUER, N. A. (1960). *Nature, Lond.*, **188**, 471. (*20, 37*)

38 BAYLISS, N. S. (1956). *Aust. J. Biol. Sci.*, **9**, 364. (*108*)

39 BECKING, J. H. (1959). *Plant and Soil*, **11**, 193. (*73*)

40 — (1961*a*). *Plant and Soil.* **15**, 217. (*51*)

41 — (1961*b*). *Plant and Soil*, **14**, 49. (*73, 84–5*)

41*a* — (1961*c*). *Plant and Soil*, **14**, 297. (*52, 73*)

42 — (1962). *Plant and Soil*, **16**, 171. (*89*)

43 — (1963). *Anton. v. Leeuwenhoek*, **29**, 326. (*77*)

44 —, DE BOER, W. E. and HOUWINK, A. L. (1964). *Anton. v. Leeuwenhoek*, **30**, 343. (*31, 33, 34, 36*)

45 BEIJERINCK, M. W. (1888). *Botan. Ztg.*, **46**, 726, 741, 757, 781, 797. (*7, 12, 23*)

46 — (1901). *Zentr. Bakteriol. Parasitenk.*, Abt. II, **7**, 561. (*7, 71*)

47 BENNETT, R., RIGOPOULOS, N. and FULLER, R. C. (1964). *Proc. Nat. Acad. Sci., U.S.A.*, **52**, 762. (*75, 107*)

48 BERGERSEN, F. J. (1958). *J. gen. Microbiol.*, **19**, 312. (*17*)

49 — (1960). *Bact. Revs.* **24**, 246. (*6, 19–21, 35, 45*)

50 — (1961). *Biochim. Biophys. Acta*, **50**, 576. (*19*)

51 — (1962*a*). *J. gen. Microbiol.*, **29**, 113. (*55–6*)

52 — (1962*b*). *Nature, Lond.*, **194**, 1059. (*20*)

53 — (1963*a*). *Aust. J. biol. Sci.*, **16**, 916. (*52*)

54 — (1963*b*). *Aust. J. biol. Sci.*, **16**, 669. (*55*)

55 — (1965). *Aust. J. biol. Sci.*, **18**, 1. (*103*)

56 —, and BRIGGS, M. J. (1958). *J. gen. Microbiol.*, **19**, 482. (*16*)

57 —, and COSTIN, A. B. (1964). *Aust. J. biol. Sci.*, **17**, 44. (*3, 36–7*)

58 —, and WILSON, P. W. (1959). *Proc. Nat. Acad. Sci., U.S.A.*, **45**, 1641. (*19, 20, 52*)

59 BERNARD, F. and LECAL, J. (1960). *Bull. Inst. Oceanog. Monaco.* No. **1166**. (*133*)

60 BERTHELOT, M. (1885). *Comp. rena. Acad. Sci. Paris*, **101**, 775. (*1, 71*)

61 BIEBERDORF, F. W. (1938). *J. Amer. Soc. Agron.*, **30**, 375. (*14*)

62 BJÄLFVE, G. (1962). *Physiol. Plant.*, **15**, 122. (*70*)

63 BHASKARAN, S. and VENKATARAMAN, G. S. (1958). *Nature, Lond.*, **181**, 277. (*70*)

64 BLOM, J. (1931). *Zentr. Bakteriol. Parasitenk.*, *Abt. II*, **84**, 60. (*100*)

65 BLOMSTROM, D. C., KNIGHT, Jr., E., PHILLIPS, W. D., and WEIHER, J. F. (1964). *Proc. Nat. Acad. Sci.*, *U.S.A.*, **51**, 1085. (*91*)

66 BOGORAD, L. (1962). *Physiology and biochemistry of algae*, ed. R. A. Lewin, p. 385. New York: Academic Press. (*59*)

67 BOLLARD, E. G. (1956). *Nature, Lond.*, **178**, 1189. (*47*)

68 — (1957). *Aust. J. biol. Sci.*, **10**, 292. (*47*)

69 BOND, G. (1936). *Ann. Bot. Lond.*, **50**, 559. (*44*)

70 — (1951). *Ann. Bot. Lond.*, N.S., **15**, 447. (*26, 48–9, 128*)

71 — (1952). *Ann. Bot. Lond.*, N.S., **16**, 467. (*30*)

72 — (1956a). *J. exp. Bot.*, **7**, 387. (*45*)

73 — (1956b). *New Phytol.*, **55**, 147. (*126*)

74 — (1957). *Ann. Bot. Lond.*, N.S., **21**, 513. (*28*)

75 — (1958). *Nutrition of the legumes*, ed. E. G. Hallsworth, p. 216. London: Butterworths. (*26–7*)

76 — (1959a). *Symp. Soc. exp. Biol.*, **13**, 59. (*26–7, 54*)

77 — (1959b). *Adv. Sci.*, **60**, 382. (*4, 36, 70*)

78 — (1960). *J. exp. Bot.*, **11**, 91. (*42, 56*)

79 — (1961). *Zeit. allg. Mikrobiol.*, **1**, 93. (*55*)

80 — (1963). *Symp. Soc. gen. Microbiol.*, **13**, 72. (*4, 6, 26–7*)

81 — (1964). *Nature, Lond.*, **204**, 600. (*45*)

82 —, and HEWITT, E. J. (1962). *Nature, Lond.*, **195**, 94. (*50*)

83 —, and SCOTT, G. D. (1955). *Ann. Bot. Lond.*, N.S., **19**, 65, (*67–8*)

84 BORTELS, H. (1930). *Arch. Mikrobiol.*, **1**, 333. (*89*)

85 — (1940). *Arch. Mikrobiol.*, **11**, 155. (*62*)

86 BOUSSINGAULT, J. B. (1838). *Ann. Chim. et Phys.*, 2nd Ser., **67**, 5. (*1, 12*)

87 — (1844). *Rural Economy*. Translated by G. Law. New York: Orange Judd. (*12, 121*)

88 — (1855). *Ann. Chim. et Phys.*, 3rd Ser., **43**, 149. (*12*)

89 BREDEMANN, G. (1908). *Centr. Bakteriol. Parasitenk.*, *Abt. II*, **22**, 44. (*77*)

90 BREED, R. S., MURRAY, E. G. D., and SMITH, N. R. (1957). *Bergey's Manual of Determinative Bacteriology*, 7th ed. London: Baillière, Tindall & Cox. (*72–3*)

91 BRIZI, U. (1908). *Ann. dell. Instit. Agr. Dott. A. Buti*, **7**, 104. (from ref. 555). (*131*)

92 BROWN, M. E. and METCALFE, G. (1957). *Nature, Lond.*, **180**, 282. (*2, 83*)

93 BRYAN, W. W. (1962). *A review of nitrogen in the tropics with particular reference to pastures. A symposium*, p. 147. Commonwealth Agricultural Bureaux, England. (*120*)

94 BUCHANAN, B. B., BACHOFEN, R. and ARNON, D. I. (1964). *Proc. Nat. Acad. Sci.*, *U.S.A.*, **52**, 839. (*111*)

95 BULEN, V. A., BURNS, R. C. and LE COMPTE, J. R. (1964). *Biochem.* *Biophys. Res. Comm.*, **17**, 265. (*5, 79, 93, 99, 113–14*)

96 —, —, — (1965). *Proc. Nat. Acad. Sci., U.S.A.*, **53**, 532. (*79, 107, 109, 113*)

97 BUNT, J. S. (1961). *Nature, Lond.*, **192**, 1275. (*59*)

98 BUNTING, A. H. and HORROCKS, J. (1964). *Ann. Bot., Lond.* N.S., **28**, 229. (*43*)

99 BURK, D. and BURRIS, R. H. (1941). *Ann. Rev. Biochem.*, **10**, 587. (*103*)

100 —, and HORNER, C. K. (1936). *Soil Sci.*, **41**, 81. (*103*)

101 —, — (1935). *Naturwiss.*, **23**, 259. (*99*)

102 —, LINEWEAVER, H. and HORNER, C. K. (1934). *J. Bacter.*, **27**, 325. (*73, 85*)

103 BURKHART, A. (1943). *Las Leguminosas argentinas.* Buenos Aires: Acme Agency, Soc. de Resp. Ltda. (*4*)

104 BURRIS, R. H. (1956). *Inorganic nitrogen metabolism*, ed. W. D. McElroy and B. Glass, p. 316. Baltimore: Johns Hopkins Press. (*6, 28*)

105 —, and MILLER, C. E. (1941). *Science*, **93**, 114. (*6*)

106 —, EPPLING, F. J., WAHLIN, H. B. and WILSON, P. W. (1943). *J. biol. Chem.*, **148**, 349. (*60, 62*)

107 —, MAGEE, W. E. and BACH, M. K. (1955). *Ann. Acad. Sci. Fenn. Ser. AII* **60**, 190. (*54–5, 92*)

108 —, and WILSON, P. W. (1945). *Ann. Rev. Biochem.*, **14**, 685. (*103*)

109 —, — (1946). *Bot. Gaz.*, **108**, 254. (*92, 94*)

110 —, — (1957). *Methods in Enzymology*, ed. S. Colowick and N. O. Kaplan, vol. 4, p. 355. New York: Academic Press. (*8, 10*)

111 —, — (1946). *J. Bacter.*, **52**, 505. (*95*)

112 —, and WANG, L. C. (1960). *Plant Physiol.*, **35**, suppl. xi. (*79*)

113 BURSTRÖM, H. (1951). *Plant Growth Substances*, ed. F. Skoog, p. 36. Madison: University of Wisconsin Press. (*14*)

114 BUTLER, G. W. and BATHURST, N. O. (1956). *7th Inter. Grassland Cong. Palmerston North, N.Z. Paper* No. **14**. (*122*)

115 CAMERON, R. E. (1962). *Trans. Amer. Micros. Soc.*, **81**, 379. (*133*)

116 —, and FULLER, W. H. (1960). *Soil Sci. Soc. Amer. Proc.*, **24**, 353. (*133*)

117 CARNAHAN, J. E., MORTENSON, L. E., MOWER, H. F., and CASTLE, J. E. (1960a). *Biochim. Biophys. Acta.*, **38**, 188. (*6, 78–9, 105*)

118 —, —, —, — (1960b). *Biochim. Biophys. Acta*, **44**, 520. (*6, 78–9, 105, 108*)

119 —, and CASTLE, J. E. (1963). *Ann. Rev. Pl. Physiol.*, **14**, 125. (*7*)

120 CENTIFANTO, Y. M. and SILVER, W. S. (1964). *J. Bacter.*, **88**, 776. (*82*)

121 CHAPMAN, H. D., LIEBIG, G. F., and RAYNER, D. S. (1949). *Hilgardia*, **19**, 57. (*128*)

122 CHAPMAN, J. A. and SALTON, M. R. J. (1962). *Arch. Mikrobiol.*, **44**, 311. (*59*)

123 CHAUDHARY, M. T., WILSON, T. G. G. and ROBERTS, E. R. (1954). *Biochim. Biophys. Acta*, **14**, 507. (*98*)

124 CHEN, H. K. and THORNTON, H. G. (1940). *Proc. roy. Soc.*, B., **129**, 208. (*16, 19*)

125 CHIBNALL, A. C., REES, M. W. and WILLIAMS, E. F. (1943). *Biochem. J.*, 37, 354. (*8*)

126 COBB, H. D. (1963). *Ph.D. Thesis, University of Texas.* (*96*)

127 COHEN, G. N. and COHEN-BAZIRE, G. (1948). *Comp. rend. Acad. Sci., Paris*, 227, 873. (*100*)

128 CONWAY, E. J. (1960). *Microdiffusion Analysis and Volumetric Error.* London: Crosby, Lockwood. (*9*)

129 COX, R. M., FAY, P. and FOGG, G. E. (1964). *Biochim. Biophys. Acta*, 88, 208. (*60, 64–5, 80*)

130 — (1965). *Ph.D. thesis, University of London.* (*10, 79, 86, 93, 107, 108*)

131 CROCKER, R. L. and MAJOR, J. (1955). *J. Ecol.*, 43, 427. (*37, 126, 131*)

132 CROFT, W. N. and GEORGE, E. A. (1959). *Bull. Brit. Mus. (Nat. Hist.). Geol.*, 3, 10. (*5*)

133 DART, P. J. and MERCER, F. V. (1964). *Arch. Mikrobiol.*, 49, 209. (*15*)

134 —, — (1963a). *J. Bacter.*, 85, 951. (*16*)

135 —, — (1963b). *Arch. Mikrobiol.*, 46, 382. (*16*)

136 —, — (1963c). *Arch. Mikrobiol.*, 47, 1. (*16*)

137 —, — (1964). *Arch. Mikrobiol.*, 47, 344. (*17, 53*)

138 DAVENPORT, H. E. (1960). *Nature, Lond.*, 186, 653. (*36*)

139 DAVIS, J. B., COTY, V. F. and STANLEY, J. P. (1964). *J. Bacter.*, 88, 468. (*76*)

140 DAVY, H. (1836). *Elements of agricultural chemistry*, 5th ed. London: Longmans. (*1*)

141 DE, P. K. (1939). *Proc. roy. Soc. B.*, 127, 121. (*62*)

142 —, and MANDAL, L. N. (1956). *Soil Sci.*, 81, 453. (*119, 128–9, 131*)

143 DELWICHE, C. C. and WIJLER, J. (1956). *Plant and Soil*, 7, 113. (*119*)

144 DERX, H. G. (1950). *Kon. Ned. Akad. Wetenschap. Proc.*, 53, 140. (*73*)

145 — (1953). *Proc. 6th Intern. Congr. Microbiol. Rome*, 6, 354. (*73*)

146 D'EUSTACHIO, A. J. and HARDY, R. W. F. (1964). *Biochem. Biophys. Res. Commun.*, 15, 319. (*109*)

147 DHAR, N. R. (1953). *J. Indian Chem. Soc.*, 30, 295. (*2*)

148 — (1958). *Indian Agric.*, 2, 57. (*2*)

149 — (1959). *Nature, Lond.*, 183, 513. (*117*)

150 DICKSON, B. A. and CROCKER, R. L. (1953). *J. Soil. Sci.*, 4, 123. (*128*)

151 DIXON, R. O. D. (1964). *Arch. Mikrobiol.*, 48, 166. (*15, 16*)

152 DÖBEREINER, J. and RUSCHEL, A. P. (1961). *Rev. Brasil. Biol.*, 21, 397. (*136*)

153 DOMMERGUES, Y. (1963). *Agrochimica*, 7, 335. (*127–8*)

154 DONALD, C. M. (1960). *J. Aust. Inst. Agric. Sci.*, 26, 319. (*5*)

155 DOUIN, R. (1953). *Comp. rend. Acad. Sci. Paris*, 236, 956. (*68*)

156 DREWES, K. (1928). *Zentr. Bakteriol. Parasitenk. Abt. II.*, 76, 88 (*2, 60, 62*)

157 DROVER, D. P. (1956). *J. Soil Sci.*, 7, 219. (*137*)

158 —, and BARRETT-LENARD, I. P. (1956). *J. Aust. Inst. Agric. Sci.*, 22, 193. (*137*)

159 DUGDALE, V. A. and DUGDALE, R. C. (1962). *Limnol. Oceanogr.*, 7, 170. (*119, 135*)

160 DUGDALE, V. A., GOERING, J. J. and RYTHER, J. (1964). *Limnol. Oceanogr.*, **9**, 507. *(61, 133)*

161 DUGDALE, R. C., MENZEL, D. W. and RYTHER, J. H. (1961). *Deep-Sea Res.*, **7**, 298. *(61)*

162 —, and NEES, J. C. (1960). In: *Trans. Semin. Algae and Metropolitan Wastes*. U.S. Pub. Health Serv., Cincinnati, Ohio. *(119)*

163 DURRELL, L. W. (1962). *Trans. Amer. Microscop. Soc.*, **80**, 73. *(133)*

163a ECHLIN, P. and MORRIS, I. (1965). *Biol. Revs.*, **40**, 143. *(59, 74)*

164 EDWARDS, M. R. and STEVENS, R. W. (1963). *J. Bacter.*, **86**, 414. *(33)*

165 EGLE, K. and MUNDING, H. (1951). *Naturwiss.*, **38**, 548. *(36)*

166 ELLISON, W. (1958). *Nutrition of the legumes*, ed. E. G. Hallsworth, p. 308. London: Butterworths. *(122–3)*

167 ESPOSITO, R. G. and WILSON, P. W. (1956). *Proc. Soc. Exp. Biol. Med.*, **93**, 564. *(90)*

168 —, — (1958). *Proc. Nat. Acad. Sci., U.S.A.*, **44**, 472. *(53)*

169 FABER, F. C. VON. (1912). *Jahrb. f. Wiss. Bot.*, **51**, 285. *(82)*

170 — (1914). *Jahrb. f. Wiss. Bot.*, **54**, 243. *(82)*

171 FÅHRAEUS, G. (1957). *J. gen. Microbiol.*, **16**, 374. *(15)*

172 —, and LJUNGGREN, H. (1959). *Physiol. Plant.*, **12**, 145. *(14)*

173 FAIRHURST, A. S., KING, H. K. and SEWELL, C. E. (1956). *J. gen. Microbiol.*, **15**, 106. *(111)*

174 FALK, J. E., APPLEBY, C. A. and PORRA, R. J. (1959). *Symp. Soc. exp. Biol.*, **12**, 73. *(20)*

175 FAY, P. Unpublished. *(79)*

176 —, and FOGG, G. E. (1962). *Arch. Mikrobiol.*, **42**, 310. *(61–2, 65, 86, 107)*

177 —, KUMAR, H. D. and FOGG, G. E. (1964). *J. gen. Microbiol.*, **35**, 351. *(61)*

178 FAY, P. and WALSBY, A. E. (1965). *Nature, Lond.* (in press). *(64)*

179 FEDOROV, M. V. (1945). *Comp. rend. Acad. Sci., U.R.S.S.* **49**, 675. *(95)*

180 FERGUSON, T. P. and BOND, G. (1953). *Ann. Bot. Lond.*, N.S. **17**, 175. *(31)*

181 FEWSON, C. A. and NICHOLAS, D. J. D. (1960). *Nature, Lond.*, **188**, 794. *(98)*

182 FLETCHER, W. W. (1955). *Ann. Bot., Lond.*, N.S., **19**, 501. *(29, 31, 33, 35)*

183 FOGG, G. E. (1942). *J. exp. Biol.*, **19**, 78. *(60, 62)*

184 — (1944). *New Phytol.*, **43**, 164. *(64)*

185 — (1949). *Ann. Bot., Lond.*, N.S. **13**, 23. *(60)*

186 — (1951a). *J. exp. Bot.*, **2**, 117. *(5, 62)*

187 — (1951b). *Ann. Bot., Lond.*, N.S., **15**, 23. *(64)*

188 — (1952). *Proc. roy. Soc.*, B., **139**, 372. *(65)*

189 — (1956a). *Ann. Rev. Plant Physiol.*, **7**, 51. *(58, 61)*

190 — (1956b). *Bact. Revs.*, **20**, 148. *(5, 58–9)*

191 — (1962a). *Physiology and biochemistry of algae*, ed. R. A. Lewin, p. 161. New York: Academic Press. *(58)*

192 — (1962b). *Physiology and biochemistry of algae*, ed. R. A. Lewin, p. 475. New York: Academic Press. *(65)*

193 —, and WOLFE, M. (1954). *Symp. Soc. gen. Microbiol.*, **4**, 99. *(58, 61, 134)*

194   FOGG, G. E. and WESTLAKE, D. F. (1955). *Verh. Internat. Verein. Limnol.*, **12**, 219. (*80*)

195   —, and THAN-TUN (1960). *Proc. roy. Soc. B.*, **153**, 111. (*61, 85–7, 107*)

196   —, and STEWART, W. D. P. (1965). *Sci. Progress*, **53**, 191. (*58*)

197   FORSTER, H. C. (1950). *J. Aust. Inst. Agric. Sci.*, **14**, 44. (*137*)

198   FRANK, B. (1890). *Landwirtsch. Jahrb.*, **19**, 523. (*12*)

199   — (1891). *Ber. dtsch. bot. Ges.*, **9**, 244. (*44*)

200   FRAZER, H. (1942). *Proc. roy. Soc. Edinb.* B. 61, **43**, 328. (*17*)

201   FRED, E. B., BALDWIN, I. L., and MCCOY, E. (1932). *Root nodule bacteria and leguminous plants.* Madison: University of Wisconsin. (*6, 11, 12, 24, 49, 119–20*)

202   FRÉMY, P. (1934). *Mém. Soc. nat. Sci. Mat. Cherbourg*, **41**, 1. (*133*)

203   FRITSCH, F. E. (1945). *The structure and reproduction of the algae*, **2**. Cambridge: Cambridge University Press. (*58–9, 64, 70, 133*)

204   — (1951). *Proc. Linn. Soc. Lond.*, **162**, 194. (*64*)

205   FUJITA, Y. and MYERS, J. (1964). *Plant Physiol.*, **39**, suppl. xii. (*65, 112*)

206   —, OHAMA, H. and HATTORI, A. (1964). *Plant and Cell Physiol.*, **5**, 305. (*93, 112*)

207   FUNKE, C. (1957). *Naturwiss.*, **44**, 498. (*17*)

208   FURMAN, T. E. (1959). *Amer. J. Bot.*, **46**, 698. (*31*)

209   GARCIA-RIVERA, J. (1961). *Ph.D. thesis, Univ. of Wisconsin.* (*99, 101*)

210   —, and BURRIS, R. H. (1962). *Fed. Proc.*, **21**, 399. (*99, 101*)

211   GARDNER, I. C. (1965). *Arch. Mikrobiol.*, **51**, 365. (*33–4*)

212   —, and BOND, G. (1957). *Canad. J. Bot.*, **35**, 305. (*35*)

213   —, and LEAF, G. (1960). *Plant Physiol.*, **35**, 948. (*47*)

214   GÄUMANN, E., JAAG, O. and ROTH, S. (1945). *Ber. schweiz. botan. Ges.*, **55**, 270. (*42–3*)

215   GEITLER, L. (1921). *Sitzber. Akad. wiss. Wien. Math-Nat Kl. 1*, **130**, 223. (*64*)

216   GEORGI, C. E. (1935). *J. Agric. Res.*, **51**, 597. (*42*)

217   —, and BEGUIN, A. E. (1939). *Nature, Lond.*, **143**, 25. (*14*)

218   GERLOFF, G. C., FITZGERALD, G. P. and SKOOG, F. (1950). *Amer. J. Bot.*, **37**, 216. (*59*)

219   GEST, H., JUDIS, J. and PECK, H. D. (1956). *Inorganic nitrogen metabolism*, ed. W. D. McElroy and B. Glass, p. 298. Baltimore: Johns Hopkins Press. (*107*)

220   —, KAMEN, M. D. and BREGOFF, H. M. (1950). *J. Biol. Chem.*, **182**, 153. (*112*)

221   —, SAN PIETRO, A. and VERNON, L. P. (1963). *Bacterial photosynthesis.* Yellow Springs, Ohio: Antioch Press. (*74*)

222   GIBSON, A. H. and NUTMAN, P. S. (1960). *Ann. Bot. Lond.*, N.S., **24**, 420. (*14*)

223   GIESY, R. M. (1964). *Amer. J. Bot.*, **51**, 388. (*59*)

224   GOLDMAN, C. R. (1961). *Ecology*, **42**, 282. (*127*)

225   GOLDSCHMIDT, V. M. (1954). *Geochemistry.* London: Oxford University Press. (*137*)

226 GOOD, R. (1953). *The geography of the flowering plants*, Second edition. London: Longmans, Green. (*4*)

227 GORHAM, P. R., MCLACHLAN, J., HAMMER, U. T. and KIM, W. K. (1964). *Verh. Internat. Verein. Limnol.*, **15**, 796. (*62, 134*)

228 GRANICK, S. (1943). *J. biol. Chem.*, **149**, 157. (*52*)

229 GRAU, F. H. (1961). *Ph.D. thesis, University of Wisconsin*. (*77, 79*)

230 —, and WILSON, P. W. (1962). *J. Bacter.*, **83**, 490. (*77, 92*)

231 GREEN, M. and WILSON, P. W. (1953). *J. Bacter.*, **65**, 511. (*112*)

232 —, ALEXANDER, M. and WILSON, P. W. (1953). *Proc. Soc. Expt. Biol. Med.*, **82**, 351. (*113*)

233 GREEN, S. and MAZUR, A. (1956). *Science*, **125**, 1150. (*52*)

234 GUKOVA, M. M. (1945). *Trudy S-kh Akad. Timiryazeva*, **30**, 33. (*48*)

235 HALLSWORTH, E. G., WILSON, S. B. and ADAMS, W. A. (1965). *Nature, Lond.*, **205**, 307. (*50*)

236 HAMILTON, P. B., SHUG. A. L., and WILSON, P. W. (1957). *Proc. Nat. Acad. Sci., U.S.A.*, **43**, 297. (*20, 52*)

237 —, and WILSON, P. W. (1955). *Ann. Acad. Sci. Fenn. Ser. A.II.* **60**, 139. (*77*)

238 HAMILTON, I. R., BURRIS, R. H. and WILSON, P. W. (1964). *Proc. Nat. Acad. Sci., U.S.A.*, **52**, 637. (*78, 80*)

239 HANADA, K. (1954). *Jap. J. Bot.*, **14**, 235. (*82*)

240 HARDER, R. (1917). *Z. Botan.*, **9**, 145. (*70*)

241 HARDY, R. W. F. and D'EUSTACHIO, A. J. (1964). *Biochem. Biophys. Res. Commun.*, **15**, 314. (*109*)

242 HARRIS, G. P. and MORRISON, T. M. (1958). *Nature, Lond.*, **182**, 1812. (*126*)

243 HARRISON, F. (1913). *Roman farm management*. New York and London: Macmillan. (*11*)

244 HATTORI, A. (1962a). *Plant and Cell Physiol.*, **3**, 355. (*101*)

245 — (1962b). *Plant and Cell Physiol.*, **3**, 371. (*101*)

246 HAWKER, L. E. and FRAYMOUTH, J. (1951). *J. gen. Microbiol.*, **5**, 369. (*31*)

247 HELLREIGEL, H. (1886). *Z. Ver. Rübenzucker-Ind. dtsch. Reichs.*, **36**, 863. (*1*)

248 — (1887). *Landw. Vers. Sta.*, **33**, 464. (*1*)

249 —, and WILFARTH, H. (1888). *Beilage. zu der Ztschr. Ver. Rübenzucker-Ind. dtsch. Reichs.* (*1, 12*)

250 HENRIKSSON, E. (1951). *Physiol. Plant.*, **4**, 542. (*62, 67*)

251 — (1957). *Physiol. Plant.*, **10**, 943. (*67*)

252 HENZELL, E. F. and NORRIS, D. O. (1962). *A review of nitrogen in the tropics with a particular reference to pastures. A symposium*, p. 1. Commonwealth Agricultural Bureaux, England. (*120*)

253 HÉRISSET, A. (1952). *Bull. Soc. Chim. biol., Paris*, **34**, 532. (*62*)

254 HEWITT, E. J. (1958). *Nutrition of the legumes*, ed. E. G. Hallsworth, p. 15. London: Butterworths. (*51*)

255 — (1958). *Nutrition of the legumes*, ed. E. G. Hallsworth, p. 254. London: Butterworths. (*52*)

256   HEWITT, E. J. (1959). *Biol. Revs.*, **39**, 333. *(51)*

257   —, BOLLE-JONES, E. W. and MILES, P. (1954). *Plant and Soil*, **5**, 205. *(51)*

258   —, and BOND, G. (1961). *Plant and Soil*, **14**, 159. *(51)*

259   —, and MILES, P. (1952). *Long Ashton Research Station Annual Report*, 199. *(51)*

260   HILLER, A., PLAZIN, T. and VAN SLYKE, D. D. (1948). *J. biol. Chem.*, **176**, 1401. *(8)*

261   HILTNER, L. (1898). *Forstl. Naturw. Z.*, **7**, 415. *(27)*

262   HOCH, G. E., LITTLE, H. N. and BURRIS, R. H. (1957). *Nature, Lond.*, **179**, 430. *(55)*

263   HOCH, and WESTLAKE, D. W. S. (1958). *Fed. Proc.*, **17**, 243. *(78)*

264   HOLM-HANSEN, O. (1963). *Science*, **139**, 1059. *(61, 88)*

265   — (1964). *Phycologia*, **4**, 43. *(61, 133)*

266   —, GERLOFF, G. C. and SKOOG, F. (1954). *Physiol. Plant.*, **7**, 665. *(88)*

267   HOPKINS, E. W. (1935). *Soil Sci.*, **39**, 297. *(42)*

268   HOUGH, L., JONES, J. K. N. and WADMAN, W. H. (1952). *J. Chem. Soc.*, p. 3393. *(59)*

269   HUGHES, D. E. (1951). *Brit. J. Exptl. Pathol.*, **32**, 97. *(78)*

270   HUMM, H. J. (1944). *J. New York Bot. Gard.*, **45**, 193. *(81)*

271   HUTCHINSON, G. E. (1944). *Amer. Sci.*, **32**, 178. *(134)*

272   JAIYEBO, E. O. and MOORE, A. W. (1963). *Nature, Lond.*, **197**, 317. *(128)*

273   JENSEN, H. L. (1943). *Proc. Linn. Soc., N.S.W.*, **68**, 207. *(49)*

274   — (1946). *Proc. Linn. Soc., N.S.W.*, **70**, 203. *(51)*

275   — (1944). *Proc. Linn. Soc., N.S.W.*, **69**, 229. *(49)*

276   — (1947). *Proc. Linn. Soc., N.S.W.*, **72**, 299. *(51)*

277   — (1947). *Proc. Linn. Soc., N.S.W.*, **72**, 265. *(49)*

278   — (1950). *Trans. 4th Internat. Congr. Soil Sci., Amsterdam*, **1**, 165. *(136)*

279   — (1958). *Nutrition of the legumes*, ed. E. G. Hallsworth, p. 75. London: Butterworths. *(73)*

280   —, and BETTY, R. C. (1943). *Proc. Linn. Soc., N.S.W.*, **68**, 1. *(51)*

281   —, and FRITH, D. (1944). *Proc. Linn. Soc., N.S.W.*, **69**, 210. *(124)*

282   —, PETERSEN, E. J., DE, P. K. and BHATTACHARYA, R. (1960). *Arch. Mikrobiol.*, **36**, 182. *(74)*

283   JENSEN, V. (1956). *Physiol. Plant.*, **9**, 130. *(77)*

284   — (1958). *Arch. Mikrobiol.*, **29**, 348. *(76)*

285   JODIN, C. R. (1862). *Comp. rend. Acad. Sci., Paris*, **55**, 612. *(1, 10, 71)*

286   JONES, W. N. and SMITH, M. L. (1928). *Brit. J. exp. Biol.*, **6**, 167. *(82)*

287   JORDAN, D. C. (1952). *Canad. J. Bot.*, **30**, 125. *(24)*

288   —, GRINYER, I. and COULTER, W. H. (1963). *J. Bacter.*, **86**, 125. *(16)*

289   JOSÉ, Jr., A. G., and WILSON, P. W. (1959). *Proc. Nat. Acad. Sci., U.S.A.*, **45**, 692. *(78)*

290   KAMEN, M. D. and GEST, H. (1949). *Science*, **109**, 560. *(71, 93, 112)*

291   KEELER, R. F. and VARNER, J. E. (1957). *Arch. Biochem. Biophys.*, **70**, 585. *(52)*

292   KEFFORD, N. P., BROCKWELL, J. and ZWAR, J. A. (1960). *Aust. J. biol. Sci.*, **13**, 456. *(14)*

293   KEILIN, D. (1953). *Nature, Lond.*, **172**, 390. *(83)*

294 KEILIN, D. and TISSIÈRES, A. (1953). *Nature, Lond.*, **172**, 393. *(83)*

295 KELLY, M. R. (1964). *Phil. Trans. Roy. Soc. B.*, **247**, 533. *(4)*

296 KJELDAHL, J. (1883). *Z. anal. Chem.*, **22**, 366. *(7)*

297 KLECZKOWSKA, J. (1950). *J. gen. Microbiol.*, **4**, 298. *(24)*

297a —, NUTMAN, P. S., and BOND, G. (1944). *J. Bacter.*, **48**, 673. *(24)*

298 KLIEWER, M. and EVANS, H. J. (1963a). *Plant Physiol.*, **38**, 99. *(50, 88)*

299 —, — (1963b). *Plant Physiol.*, **38**, 55. *(50–1)*

300 KNIGHT, Jr., E. and BLOMSTROM, D. C. (1964). *Biochim. Biophys. Acta*, **89**, 553. *(91)*

301 KOHNKE, H. (1941). *J. Forest.*, **39**, 333. *(125)*

302 KOSTYTSCHEW, S., RYSKALTSCHUK, A. and SCHWEZOWA, O. (1926). *Zeit. Physiol. Chem. Hoppe Seyler's*, **154**, I. *(103)*

303 KRASILNIKOV, N. A. (1956). *Uspekhi. Sovr. Biol.*, **41**, 177. *(132)*

304 KRATZ, W. A. and MYERS, J. (1955). *Amer. J. Bot.*, **42**, 282. *(60, 86, 107)*

304a KROONTJE, W. and KEHR, W. R. (1956). *Agron. J.*, **48**, 127. *(122–3)*

305 KUMAR, H. D. (1962). *Nature, Lond.*, **196**, 1121. *(59)*

306 KUSNEZOW, S. I. (1959). *Die Rolle der Mikroorganismen im Stoffkreislauf der Seen.* Berlin. *(136)*

307 LACHMANN, J. (1858). *Landw. Mitt. Z. Kaiserl. Lehranst. Vers. Sta. Poppelsdorf (Bonn)*, p. 37. *(23)*

307a LALORAYA, V. K. and MITRA, A. K. (1964). *Curr. Sci.*, **33**, 619. *(62)*

308 LAMI, R. and MESLIN, R. (1959). *Bull. Lab. Marit. Dinard*, **44**, 47. *(70)*

309 LAWRENCE, D. B. (1958). *Amer. Sci.*, **46**, 89. *(37, 127–8)*

310 LAZAROFF, N. and VISHNIAC, W. (1962). *J. gen. Microbiol.*, **28**, 203. *(59)*

311 LEAF, G., GARDNER, I. C. and BOND, G. (1958). *J. exp. Bot.*, **9**, 320. *(47, 111)*

312 LEES, H. (1955). *Biochemistry of Autotrophic Bacteria.* London: Butterworths. *(74)*

313 LEITGEB, H. (1878). *Sitzber. Akad. wiss. Wien. Math-Nat. Kl.*, *1*, **77**, 411. *(68)*

314 LEVIN, A. P., FUNK, H. B. and TENDLER, M. D. (1954). *Science*, **120**, 784. *(51)*

315 LHOTSKY, S. (1946). *Stud. Botan. Čechoslov.*, **7**, 20. *(68)*

316 LIFE, A. C. (1901). *Bot. Gaz.*, **31**, 265. *(70)*

317 LIND, C. J. and WILSON, P. W. (1941). *J. Amer. Chem. Soc.*, **63**, 3511. *(56)*

318 LINDSTROM, E. S., BURRIS, R. H. and WILSON, P. W. (1949). *J. Bacter.*, **58**, 313. *(71)*

319 —, LEWIS, S. M. and PINSKY, M. J. (1951). *J. Bacter.*, **61**, 481. *(71, 83)*

320 —, NEWTON, J. W. and WILSON, P. W. (1952). *Proc. Nat. Acad. Sci., U.S.A.*, **38**, 392. *(71)*

321 —, TOVE, S. R. and WILSON, P. W. (1950). *Science*, **112**, 197. *(71, 75)*

322 LINKO, P., HOLM-HANSEN, O., BASSHAM, J. A. and CALVIN, M. (1957). *J. exp. Bot.*, **8**, 147. *(112)*

323 LIPMAN, J. G. (1912). *N.J. Agric. Exp. Sta. Bull.*, No. **253**. *(43)*

324 —, and CONEYBEARE, A. B. (1936). *N.J. Agric. Exp. Sta. Bull.*, No. **607**. *(5)*

324*a* LOSADA, M., WHATLEY, F. R. and ARNON, D. I. (1961). *Nature, Lond.*, **190**, 606. (*90*)

325 LOWE, R. H. and EVANS, H. J. (1961). *Plant. Physiol.*, **36**, 545. (*20*)

326 LUDWIG, C. A. and ALLISON, F. E. (1935). *J. Amer. Soc. Agron.*, **27**, 895. (*13*)

327 LYON, T. L. (1936). *Cornell Univ. Agric. Exp. Sta. Bull.*, No. **645**. (*124*)

328 MAGEE, W. E. and BURRIS, R. H. (1954). *Amer. J. Bot.*, **41**, 777. (*60*)

329 —, — (1956). *J. Bacter.*, **71**, 635. (*78*)

330 MALPIGHI, M. (1675). *Anatome plantarum*, London. (*11*)

331 MACCONNEL, J. T. and BOND, G. (1957). *Ann. Bot. Lond.*, N.S. **21**, 185. (*119*)

332 MCKEE, H. S. (1962). *Nitrogen metabolism in plants*. Oxford: Clarendon Press. (*6*)

333 MCKENZIE, H. A. and WALLACE, H. S. (1954). *Aust. J. Chem.*, **7**, 55. (*8*)

334 MCLUCKIE, J. (1922). *Proc. Linn. Soc., N.S.W.*, **47**, 319. (*70*)

335 — (1923). *Proc. Linn. Soc., N.S.W.*, **48**, 82. (*37*)

336 MCNARY, J. and BURRIS, R. H. (1962). *J. Bacter.*, **84**, 598. (*108*)

337 MEEUSE, B. J. D. (1962). *Physiology and biochemistry of algae*, ed. R. A. Lewin, p. 289. New York: Academic Press. (*59*)

338 MENKE, W. (1961). *Z. Naturforsch.*, **16**b, 543. (*59*)

339 MES, M. G. (1959*a*). *S. African J. Sci.*, **55**, 35. (*48*)

340 — (1959*b*). *Nature, Lond.*, **184**, 2032. (*48*)

341 METCALFE, G. and BROWN, M. E. (1957), *J. gen. Microbiol.*, **17**, 567. (*83*)

342 —, CHAYEN, S., ROBERTS, E. R. and WILSON, T. G. G. (1954). *Nature, Lond.*, **174**, 841. (*2, 83*)

343 MIEHE, H. (1914). *Jahrb. f. Wiss. Bot.*, **53**, 1. (*82*)

344 MIETTINEN, J. K. and VIRTANEN, A. I. (1952). *Physiol. Plant.*, **5**, 540. (*47*)

345 MILNER, H. W., LAWRENCE, N. S. and FRENCH, C. S. (1950). *Science*, **111**, 633. (*78*)

346 MISHUSTIN, E. N., NAUMOVA, A. N. and MARENKO, V. G. (1964). *Izv. timiryazev. s-kh. Akad.*, **3**, 174. (*136*)

347 MITRA, A. K. (1950). *Ann. Bot., Lond.*, N.S., **14**, 457. (*61*)

348 MOLISCH, H. (1925). *Sci. Rep. Tohoku Univ.*, **1**, 169. (*68*)

349 MOORE, A. W. (1963*a*). *Plant and Soil*, **19**, 127. (*128*)

350 — (1963*b*). *Plant and Soil*, **19**, 385. (*77*)

351 —, and BECKING, J. H. (1963). *Nature, Lond.*, **198**, 915. (*77*)

352 MOORE, R. T. and MCALEAR, J. H. (1960). *Mycologia*, **52**, 805. (*67*)

353 MORET, L. (1949). *Paléontologie végétale*. Paris: Masson. (*4*)

354 MORRISON, T. M. (1961). *Nature, Lond.*, **189**, 945. (*28*)

355 MORTENSON, L. E. (1961). *Anal. Biochem.*, **2**, 216. (*9*)

356 — (1962). *The Bacteria*, ed. I. C. Gunsalus and R. Y. Stanier, vol. 3, p. 119. New York: Academic Press. (*7, 85, 110*)

357 — (1963). *Ann. Rev. Microbiol.*, **17**, 115. (*7, 91, 94, 106*)

358 — (1964*a*). *Proc. Nat. Acad. Sci., U.S.A.*, **52**, 272. (*10, 79, 91, 106, 109–10*)

359 — (1964*b*). *Biochim. Biophys. Acta*, **81**, 71. (*91*)

360 — (1964*c*). *Biochim. Biophys. Acta*, **81**, 473. (*91*)

361 MORTENSON, L. E. (1964d). *Abst. 6th Internat. Congr. Biochem. N.Y.* (*91*)

362 —, MOWER, H. F. and CARNAHAN, J. E. (1962). *Bact. Revs.*, **26**, 42. (*7, 79, 103, 105, 113*)

363 —, and SIZELOVE, J. C. (1963). *Fed. Proc.*, **22**, 355. (*106*)

364 —, VALENTINE, R. C. and CARNAHAN, J. E. (1962). *Biochem. Biophys. Res. Commun.*, **7**, 448. (*90*)

365 —, —, — (1963). *J. biol. Chem.*, **238**, 794. (*114*)

366 MOSSE, B. (1964). *J. gen. Microbiol.*, **36**, 49. (*15, 16*)

367 MOSTAFA, M. A. and MAHMOUD, M. Z. (1951), *Nature, Lond.*, **167**, 446. (*37*)

368 MOZEN, M. M. (1955). *Ph.D. thesis, University of Wisconsin.* (*98*)

369 —, and BURRIS, R. H. (1954). *Biochim. Biophys. Acta*, **14**, 577. (*98*)

370 MULDER, E. G. (1948). *Plant and Soil*, **1**, 94. (*51*)

371 — (1954). *Plant and Soil*, **5**, 368. (*51*)

372 *Nature Conservancy Rep.*, *1963*, p. 78, London: H.M.S.O. (*125*)

373 NEMEC, B. (1932). *Studies from the plant physiology laboratory, Prague*, **4**, 1. (*82*)

374 NÉMETH, G. (1959). *Nature, Lond.*, **183**, 1460. (*83*)

375 —, and MATKOVICS, B. (1957). *Naturwiss.*, **44**, 621. (*83*)

376 —, URESCH, F., FODOR, G. and LÁNG, L. (1961). *Nature, Lond.*, **191**, 1413. (*83*)

377 NEWTON, J. W. and WILSON, P. W. (1953). *Anton v. Leeuwenhoek*, **19**, 71. (*93, 112*)

378 —, WILSON, P. W. and BURRIS, R. H. (1953). *J. biol. Chem.*, **204**, 445. (*66, 80, 103*)

379 NICHOLAS, D. J. D. (1958). *Nutrition of the legumes*, ed. E. G. Hallsworth, p. 239. London: Butterworths. (*6, 90–1, 113*)

380 — (1963). *Symp. Soc. gen. Microbiol.*, **13**, 92. (*7, 73, 80, 90, 104, 108*)

381 —, and FISHER, D. J. (1960a). *Nature, Lond.*, **186**, 735. (*6, 73, 78–9*)

382 —, — (1960b). *J. Sci. Food, Agric.*, **11**, 603. (*79*)

383 —, —, REDMOND, W. J. and OSBORNE, M. (1964). *Nature, Lond.*, **201**, 793. (*89*)

384 —, SILVESTER, D. J. and FOWLER, J. F. (1961). *Nature, Lond.*, **189**, 634. (*9*)

385 —, KOBAYASHI, M. and WILSON, P. W. (1962). *Proc. Nat. Acad. Sci.*, *U.S.A.*, **48**, 1537. (*89*)

386 NIEWIAROWSKA, J. (1959). *Acta Microbiol. Polonica*, **8**, 289. (*34*)

387 — (1961). *Acta Microbiol. Polonica*, **10**, 271. (*34*)

388 NILSSON, R., BJÄLFVE, G. and BURSTRÖM, D. (1938). *Naturwiss.*, **26**, 284, 661. (*23*)

389 NOBBE, F., SCHMID, E., HILTNER, L. and HOTTER, E. (1892). *Landw. Vers. Sta.*, **41**, 138. (*2, 26*)

390 —, and HILTNER, L. (1899). *Landw. Vers. Sta.*, **51**, 241. (*36*)

390a —, — (1904). *Naturw. Z. Landw. v. Forstw.*, **2**, 366. (*27*)

391 NOVAK, R. and WILSON, P. W. (1948). *J. Bacter.*, **55**, 517. (*101*)

392 NUTMAN, P. S. (1946). *Nature, Lond.*, **157**, 463. (*23*)

393 — (1948). *Ann. Bot. Lond.*, N.S., **12**, 81. (*24*)

394 — (1952). *Ann. Bot. Lond.*, N.S., **16**, 79. (*25*)

395 NUTMAN, P. S. (1954). *Heredity, Lond.*, **8**, 35, 47. *(23)*

396 — (1956). *Biol. Revs.*, **31**, 109. *(15, 24–5, 49)*

397 — (1957). *Heredity, Lond.*, **11**, 157. *(23)*

398 — (1958). *Nutrition of the legumes*, p. 87, ed. E. G. Hallsworth. London: Butterworths. *(13, 19, 24, 25)*

399 — (1959a). *Symp. Soc. Exp. Biol.*, **13**, 42. *(25)*

400 — (1959b). *J. exp. Bot.*, **10**, 250. *(14, 15)*

401 — (1963). *Symp. Soc. Gen. Microbiol.*, **13**, 51. *(6, 14, 17, 23, 25)*

402 O'HEOCHA, C. (1962) *Physiology and biochemistry of algae*, ed. R. A. Lewin, p. 421. New York: Academic Press. *(59)*

403 OKUDA, A., YAMAGUCHI, M. and NIOH, I. (1962). *Soil Sci. and Plant Nutrition*, **8**, 35. *(89)*

404 OPLIŠTILOVÁ, K. and VANČURA, V. (1963). *Úst. Věd. Inf. M.Ž.L.V.H. (Rostl. Výroba)*, **36**, 734. *(14)*

405 ORR, M. Y. (1924). *Notes Roy. bot. Gdn., Edinb.*, **14**, 57. *(81)*

406 PANKOW, H. (1964). *Naturwiss.*, **51**, 274. *(5, 62)*

407 —, and MARTENS, B. (1964). *Arch. Mikrobiol.*, **48**, 203. *(62, 68)*

408 PANKRATZ, H. S. and BOWEN, C. C. (1963). *Amer. J. Bot.*, **50**, 387. *(59)*

409 PARKER, C. A. (1954). *Aust. J. Agric. Res.*, **5**, 90. *(76)*

409a — (1957). *J. Soil Sci.*, **8**, 48. *(137)*

410 —, and SCUTT, P. B. C. (1960). *Biochim. Biophys. Acta.* **38**, 230. *(73)*

411 PATE, J. S. (1958a). *Aust. J. biol. Sci.*, **11**, 366. *(44)*

412 — (1958b). *Aust. J. biol. Sci.*, **11**, 496. *(42)*

413 — (1961). *Nature, Lond.*, **192**, 637. *(47–8)*

414 —, and WALLACE, W. (1964). *Ann. Bot., Lond.*, N.S. **28**, 83. *(46)*

415 PATTNAIK, H. (1964). *Ph.D. thesis, University of London.* *(5, 62, 66, 84, 104)*

416 PEARSALL, W. H. (1938). *J. Ecol.*, **26**, 298. *(48)*

417 PECK, H. D. and GEST, H. (1957). *J. Bacter.*, **73**, 569. *(90)*

418 PENGRA, R. M. and WILSON, P. W. (1958). *J. Bacter.*, **75**, 21. *(77, 112)*

419 —, — (1959). *Proc. Soc. Exptl. Biol. Med.*, **100**, 436. *(89)*

420 PINE, M. J. and BARKER, H. A. (1954). *J. Bacter.*, **68**, 589. *(77)*

421 PINTNER, I. J. and PROVASOLI, L. (1958). *J. gen. Microbiol.*, **18**, 1. *(59)*

422 POMMER, E. H. (1956). *Flora*, **143**, 603. *(29)*

423 — (1959). *Ber. dtsch. bot. Ges.*, **72**, 138. *(34)*

424 POSSINGHAM, J. V., MOYE, D. V. and ANDERSON, A. J. (1964). *Plant Physiol.*, **39**, 561. *(47)*

425 POWRIE, J. K. (1964). *Plant and Soil*, **21**, 81. *(120)*

426 PRASAD, S. (1949). *Jour. Proc. Inst. Chem.*, **21**, 135. *(128)*

427 PRATT, D. C. and FRENKEL, A. W. (1959). *Plant Physiol.*, **34**, 333. *(75, 107)*

428 PRATT, J. M. (1962). *J. Theoret. Biol.*, **2**, 251. *(108)*

429 PRATT, P. F., GOULBEN, B. and HARDING, R. B. (1957). *Soil Sci. Proc.*, **21**, 215. *(137)*

430 PRINGSHEIM, E. G. (1914). *Beitr. Biol. Pfl.*, **12**, 49, 295, 439. *(60)*

431 PROCTOR, M. H. and WILSON, P. W. (1958). *Nature, Lond.*, **182**, 891. *(76)*

432 — (1959). *M.S. thesis, University of Wisconsin.* *(76, 94)*

433 —, and WILSON, P. W. (1961). *Zeit. Allg. Mikrobiol.* **1**, 175. *(76, 88)*

434 PURCHASE, H. F. and NUTMAN, P. S. (1957). *Ann. Bot., Lond.*, N.S. **21**, 439. *(24)*

435 QUISPEL, A. (1955). *Acta Bot. Neerl.*, **4**, 671. *(126)*

436 — (1954). *Acta Bot. Neerl.*, **3**, 512. *(30)*

437 — (1960). *Acta Bot. Neerl.*, **9**, 380. *(34)*

438 RAGGIO, N., RAGGIO, M. and BURRIS, R. H. (1959). *Biochim. Biophys. Acta*, **32**, 274. *(43)*

439 RAGGIO, M., RAGGIO, N. and TORREY, J. A. (1957). *Amer. J. Bot.*, **44**, 325. *(43)*

440 RAO, K. (1923). *Agric. J. India*, **18**, 132. *(82)*

441 REINKE, J. (1903). *Ber. dtsch. bot. Ges.*, **21**, 481. *(80)*

442 REUTER, G. and WOLFGANG, H. (1953). *Flora*, **142**, 146. *(47)*

443 REPASKE, R. and WILSON, P. W. (1952). *J. Amer. Chem. Soc.*, **74**, 3101. *(98)*

444 RIS, H. and SINGH, R. N. (1961). *J. Biophys. Biochem. Cytol.*, **9**, 63. *(59)*

445 ROBERTS, E. R. (1959). *Symp. Soc. Exp. Biol.*, **13**, 24. *(98)*

446 ROBERTSON, A. J. B. (1954). *Mass Spectrometry*. London: Methuen. *(8)*

447 ROVIRA, A. D. (1959). *Plant and Soil*, **11**, 53. *(14)*

448 — (1962). *Soils and Fertilisers*, **25**, 167. *(14, 44)*

449 ROY, A. B. and MUKHERJEE, M. K. (1957). *Nature, Lond.*, **180**, 236. *(77, 92, 94)*

450 RUINEN, J. (1956). *Nature, Lond.*, **177**, 220. *(73, 82)*

451 — (1961). *Plant and Soil*, **15**, 81. *(73, 76, 82)*

452 RUSSELL, E. J. and RUSSELL, E. W. (1961). *Soil Conditions and Plant Growth*. London: Longmans, Green. *(136)*

453 SABET, Y. S. (1946). *Nature, Lond.*, **157**, 656. *(37)*

454 SAN PIETRO, A. (1961). *Light and Life*, ed. W. D. McElroy and B. Glass, p. 631. Baltimore: Johns Hopkins Press. *(90–1)*

455 SAUBERT, G. G. P. (1949). *Ann. bot. Gdn. Buitenz.*, **51**, 177. *(68)*

456 SAXTON, W. T. (1930). *S. Afric. J. Sci.*, **27**, 323. *(37)*

457 SCHAEDE, R. (1940). *Planta*, **31**, 1. *(14)*

458 — (1944). *Planta*, **34**, 98. *(70)*

459 — (1948). *Die pflanzlichen Symbiosen*. Jena: G. Fischer. *(31, 33, 44)*

460 SCHANDERL, H. (1947). *Botanische Bakteriologie und Stickstoffhausalt der Pflanzen*. Stuttgart: Ulmer. *(2)*

461 SCHNEIDER, A. (1894). *Bot. Gaz.*, **19**, 25. *(70)*

462 SCHNEIDER, K. C., BRADBEER, C., SINGH, R. N., WANG, L. C., WILSON, P. W. and BURRIS, R. H. (1960). *Proc. Nat. Acad. Sci., U.S.A.*, **46**, 726. *(6, 60, 64, 75, 78–9, 86)*

463 SCHWEIZER, J. (1932). *Ver. Schweiz. Naturf. Ges.*, **113**, 376. *(42)*

464 SCOTT, G. D. (1956). *New Phytol.*, **55**, 111. *(67)*

465 SHAUKAT-AHMED and EVANS, H. J. (1961). *Proc. Nat. Acad. Sci., U.S.A.*, **47**, 24. *(50)*

466 SHIELDS, L. M. and DURRELL, L. W. (1964). *Botan. Rev.*, **30**, 92. *(133)*

467 SHUG, A. L., HAMILTON, P. B. and WILSON, P. W. (1956). *Inorganic Nitrogen Metabolism*, ed. W. D. McElroy and B. Glass, p. 344. Baltimore: Johns Hopkins Press. *(90, 113)*

468   SHUG, A. L., WILSON, P. W., GREEN, D. E. and MAHLER, H. R. (1954).
      J. Amer. Chem. Soc., **76**, 3355. (*90*)
469   SILVER, W. S. (1964). *J. Bacter.*, **87**, 416. (*31, 33*)
470   —, BENDANA, F. E. and POWELL, R. D. (in press). (*30*)
471   —, CENTIFANTO, Y. M. and NICHOLAS, D. J. D. (1963). *Nature, Lond.*,
      199, 396. (*4, 81–2*)
472   SIMS, A. P. and FOLKES, B. F. (1964). *Proc. roy. Soc. B.*, **159**, 479. (*110*)
473   SIMPSON, J. B. (1936). *Proc. roy. Soc., Edinb.*, **56**, 90. (*36*)
474   SINGH, R. N. (1942). *Ind. J. Agric. Sci.*, **12**, 743. (*62*)
475   — (1961). *The role of blue-green algae in nitrogen economy of Indian agricul-
      ture.* New Delhi: Indian Council Agric. Res. (*58, 128, 130–4*)
476   SISLER, F. D. and ZOBELL, C. E. (1951). *J. Bacter.*, **62**, 117. (*77*)
477   SKINNER, C. E. (1928). *Soil Sci.*, **25**, 195. (*77*)
478   SMITH, H. V. (1944). *Tech. Bull. Ariz. agric. Exp. Sta.*, No. **102**. (*120, 128*)
479   SMITH, J. D. (1951). In: Bond, G. (1951). *Ann. Bot. Lond.*, N.S., **15**,
      447. (*36*)
480   — (1949). *Biochem. J.*, **44**, 585. (*36*)
481   SPENCER, D., TAKAHASHI, H. and NASON, A. (1957). *J. Bacter.*, **73**, 553.
      (*101*)
482   SPRATT, E. R. (1912). *Ann. Bot., Lond.*, **26**, 801. (*36*)
483   — (1915). *Ann. Bot., Lond.*, **29**, 619. (*70*)
484   STANIER, R. Y. and COHEN-BAZIRE, G. (1957). *Symp. Soc. gen. Microbiol.*,
      7, 56. (*74*)
485   —, and VAN NIEL, C. B. (1962). *Arch. Mikrobiol.*, **42**, 17. (*74*)
486   STAPP, C. (1940). *Zentr. Bakteriol. Parasitenk. Abt. II*, **102**, 1. (*76*)
487   STARKEY, R. L. and DE, P. K. (1939). *Soil Sci.*, **47**, 329. (*73*)
488   STEVENSON, G. (1958). *Nature, Lond.*, **182**, 1523. (*26, 128*)
489   — (1959). *Ann. Bot., Lond.*, N.S., **23**, 622. (*81*)
490   STEWART, W. D. P. (1962*a*). *J. exp. Bot.*, **13**, 250. (*28, 31, 35, 44–5, 127*)
491   — (1962*b*). *Ann. Bot., Lond.*, N.S., **26**, 439. (*59, 62, 70, 134*)
492   — (1963*a*). *Nature, Lond.*, **200**, 1020. (*65*)
493   — (1963*b*). *Zeit. Allg. Mikrobiol.*, **3**, 152. (*126*)
494   — (1964*a*). *J. gen. Microbiol.*, **36**, 333. (*60, 94*)
495   — (1964*b*). *J. exp. Bot.*, **15**, 138. (*60*)
496   — (1965*a*). *Ann. Bot., Lond.*, N.S., **29**, 229. (*119, 129–30, 133–4*)
497   — Unpublished. (*61, 68, 84, 119, 134*)
498   —, and BOND, G. (1961). *Plant and Soil*, **14**, 347. (*40, 126*)
499   —, and PEARSON, M. (1965). (in preparation). (*125–8*)
500   —, and PUGH, G. J. F. (1963). *J. mar. biol. Assoc., U.K.*, **43**, 309. (*134*)
501   STEWARD, F. C. and POLLARD, J. K. (1957). *Ann. Rev. Plant Physiol.*, **8**,
      65. (*98*)
502   SUZUKI, N. and SUZUKI, S. (1954). *Sci. Rep. Tohuku. Univ.* **20**, 195. (*99,
      100*)
503   TAGAWA, K. and ARNON, D. I. (1962). *Nature, Lond.*, **195**, 537. (*91*)
504   —, TSUJIMOTO, H. Y. and ARNON, D. I. (1963). *Proc. Nat. Acad. Sci.,
      U.S.A.*, **49**, 567. (*91*)
505   TANNER, J. W. and ANDERSON, I. C. (1963). *Nature, Lond.*, **198**, 303. (*43*)

506 TANSLEY, A. G. (1939). *The British Islands and their vegetation.* Cambridge: Cambridge University Press. *(4)*

507 TAHA, M. S. (1964). *Fiziologiya Rast.,* **11**, 424. *(62)*

508 TARRANT, R. F. and MILLER, R. E. (1963). *Proc. Soil Sci. Soc. Amer.,* **27**, 231. *(127)*

509 TAUBERT, H. (1956). *Planta,* **48**, 135. *(29)*

510 TCHAN, Y. T. and BEADLE, N. C. W. (1955). *J. Linn. Soc., N.S.W.,* **80**, 97. *(128, 133)*

511 TERNETZ, C. (1907). *Jahrb. f. Wiss. Bot.,* **44**, 353. *(82)*

512 THIMANN, K. V. (1939). *Trans. 3rd Comm. Int. Soc. Soil Sci.,* **A**, 24. *(14)*

513 THORNTON, H. G. (1929). *J. agric. Sci.,* **19**, 373. *(24)*

514 — (1930). *Ann. Bot., Lond.,* **44**, 385. *(16)*

515 — (1936). *Sci. Progr.,* **31**, 236. *(16)*

516 — (1939). *Trans. 3rd Comm. Int. Soc. Soil Sci.,* **A**, 20. *(19)*

517 — (1945). *Nature, Lond.,* **156**, 654. *(23)*

518 — (1936). *Proc. Roy. Soc. B.,* **119**, 474. *(43)*

519 — (1949). *Agr. Progr.,* **24**, II, 102. *(13)*

520 —, and NICOL, H. (1936). *J. Agric. Sci.,* **26**, 173. *(41)*

521 TÓTH, L. (1944). *Magyar. Biol. Kut. Munk.,* **16**, 7. *(80)*

522 — (1946). *Monographs Natural Science,* vol. 5, Budapest. *(80)*

523 — (1952). *Tijdschr. Entomol.,* **95**, 43. *(80)*

524 TREUB, M. (1888). *Ann. Jard. Bot. Buitenzorg.,* **7**, 221. *(132)*

525 TURCHIN, F. V., BERSENEVA, Z. N. and ZHIDKIKH, G. G. (1963). *Doklady Akad. Nauk. S.S.S.R.,* **149**, 731. *(2)*

526 TUTIN, T. G. (1958). *Nutrition of the legumes,* ed. E. G. Hallsworth, p. 3. London: Butterworths. *(4)*

527 UEMURA, S. (1952). *Bull. Jap. Govt. Forest Exp. Sta.,* **52**, 1. *(34–5)*

528 — (1961). *Sci. Reps. Agric. Forest and Fish. Res. Co., Tokyo,* **7**, 1. *(34)*

529 VAN BAALEN, C. (1962). *Botan. Marina,* **4**, 129. *(59)*

530 VANČURA, V., MACURA, J., FISCHER, O. and VONDRACEK, J. (1959). *Folia Microbiol.,* **4**, 110. *(136)*

531 VAN NIEL, C. B. (1944). *Bact. Revs.,* **8**, 1. *(74)*

532 — (1954). *Ann. Rev. Microbiol.,* **8**, 105. *(74)*

533 — (1962). *Ann. Rev. Plant Physiol.,* **13**, 1. *(74)*

534 VAN SCHREVEN, D. A. (1958). *Nutrition of the legumes,* ed. E. G. Hallsworth, p. 137. London: Butterworths. *(49)*

535 VENKATARAMAN, G. S. (1961). *Ind. J. Agric. Sci.,* **31**, 213. *(62)*

536 — (1962). *Ind. J. Agric. Sci.,* **32**, 22. *(62)*

537 —, DUTTA, N. and NATARAJAN, K. V. (1959). *J. Ind. Bot. Soc.,* **38**, 114. *(62, 68)*

538 —, and SAXENA, H. K. (1963). *Ind. J. Agric. Sci.,* **33**, 21. *(65, 68)*

539 VIRTANEN, A. I. (1928). *Biochem. Z.,* **193**, 300. *(29, 49)*

540 — (1938). *Cattle fodder and human nutrition.* Cambridge: Cambridge University Press. *(6, 43, 101)*

541 — (1945). *Nature, Lond.,* **155**, 747. *(52)*

542 — (1947). *Biol. Revs.,* **22**, 239. *(102)*

543 — (1948). *Ann. Rev. Microbiol.,* **2**, 485. *(6)*

544   VIRTANEN, A. I., ERKAMA, J. and LINKOLA, H. (1947). *Acta. Chem. Scand.*,
      1, 861. (*19*)
545   —, and von HAUSEN, S. (1935). *Nature, Lond.*, **135**, 184. (*45*)
546   —, JORMA, J., LINKOLA, H. and LINNASALMI, A. (1947). *Acta. Chem.
      Scand.*, **1**, 90. (*41, 43*)
547   —, von HAUSEN, S. and LAINE, T. (1937). *J. agric. Sci.*, **27**, 584. (*43*)
548   —, and LAINE, T. (1936a). *Biochem. J.*, **30**, 377. (*45*)
548a —, — (1936b). *Suomen Kemistilehti*, **B9**, 5, 12. (*100*)
549   —, — (1939). *Biochem. J.*, **33**, 412. (*43*)
550   —, LINKOLA, H., HAKALA, M. and RAUTANEN, N. (1946). *Suomen Kemis-
      tilehti*, **B19**, 83. (*43*)
551   —, and MIETTINEN, J. K. (1963). *Plant Physiology*, ed. F. C. Steward, vol.
      3, p. 539. New York: Academic Press. (*19, 43, 52, 90, 101–2, 127–8*)
552   —, MOISIO, T. and BURRIS, R. H. (1955). *Acta Chem. Scand.*, **9**, 184. (*42*)
553   VLAMIS, J., SCHULTZ, A. M. and BISWELL, H. H. (1964). *J. Range Manage-
      ment*, **17**, 73. (*37*)
554   VOETS, J. B. and DEBACKER, J. (1955). *Naturwiss.*, **43**, 40. (*76*)
554a WAGLE, R. F. and VLAMIS, J. (1961). *Ecology*, **42**, 745. (*38*)
555   WAKSMAN, S. A. (1927). *Principles of soil microbiology*. London: Baillière,
      Tindall & Cox. (*7, 60*)
556   WALKER, D. (1955). *New Phytol.*, **54**, 222. (*4*)
557   WALL, J. S., WAGENKNECHT, A. C., NEWTON, J. W. and BURRIS, R. H.
      (1952). *J. Bacter.*, **63**, 563. (*104*)
558   WALP, L. and SCHOPBACH, R. (1942). *Growth*, **6**, 33. (*61*)
559   WATANABE, A. (1951). *Arch. Biochem. Biophys.*, **34**, 50. (*62*)
560   — (1959). *J. gen. appl. Microbiol.*, *Tokyo*, **5**, 21. (*62*)
561   — (1961). *Stud. Tokugawa Inst.*, *Tokyo*, **9**, 162. (*58, 131–2*)
562   WATANABE, A., HATTORI, A., FUJITA, Y. and KIYOHARA, T. (1959).
      J. gen. appl. Microbiol., *Tokyo*, **5**, 85. (*132*)
563   — and KIYOHARA, T. (1963). *Microalgae and Photosynthetic Bacteria*,
      Tokyo, p. 189. (*67–8, 70*)
564   WEST, P. M. and WILSON, P. W. (1940). *Enzymologia*, **8**, 152. (*14, 23*)
565   WHYTE, R. O., NILSSON-LEISSNER, G. and TRUMBLE, H. C. (1953). *Legumes
      in Agriculture*. Rome: F.A.O. Agric. Stud. (*121–2, 124*)
566   WIAME, J. M. and PIÉRARD, A. (1955). *Nature, Lond.*, **176**, 1073. (*111*)
567   WIERINGA, K. T. (1958). *Nutrition of the legumes*, ed. E. G. Hallsworth,
      p. 256. London: Butterworths. (*47*)
568   WILDON, D. C. and MERCER, F. V. (1963a). *Aust. J. biol. Sci.*, **16**, 85. (*59*)
569   —, — (1963b). *Arch. Mikrobiol.*, **47**, 19. (*64*)
570   WILSDEN, B. H. and BARKAT, A. (1922). *Soil Sci.*, **14**, 127. (*128*)
571   WILKINSON, S. R. and OHLROGGE, A. J. (1964), *Nature, Lond.*, **204**,
      902. (*42*)
572   WILLIAMS, A. E. and BURRIS, R. H. (1952). *Amer. J. Bot.*, **39**, 340.
      (*60, 62, 70, 134*)
573   WILSON, H. (1920). *J. Arnold Arboretum*, **2**, 25. (*125*)
574   WILSON, J. B. and WILSON, P. W. (1942). *J. Bacter.*, **43**, 329. (23)
575   WILSON, J. K. (1931). *J. Amer. Soc. Agron.*, **23**, 670. (*42*)

576 WILSON, J. K. (1939). *Mem. Cornell. Agric. Exp. Sta.*, No. **221**. *(24)*
577 — (1944). *Soil Sci.*, **58**, 61. *(24)*
578 — (1945). *Mem. Cornell. Agric. Exp. Sta.*, No. **276**. *(24)*
579 WILSON, P. W. (1936). *J. Amer. Chem. Soc.*, **58**, 1256. *(54)*
580 — (1940). *The biochemistry of symbiotic nitrogen fixation.* Madison: University of Wisconsin Press. *(6, 11, 12, 41, 43-5)*
581 — (1951). *Bacterial physiology*, ed. C. H. Werkman and P. W. Wilson, p. 467. New York: Academic Press. *(6)*
582 — (1952). *Adv. Enzymol.*, **13**, 345. *(7, 82)*
583 — (1957). *Bact. Revs.*, **21**, 215. *(12)*
584 — (1958). *Encyclopedia of Plant Physiology*, vol. 8, p. 9. Berlin: Springer Verlag. *(6, 8, 80, 103-4, 110)*
585 —, and BURRIS, R. H. (1947). *Bact. Revs.*, **11**, 41. *(6)*
586 —, — (1953). *Ann. Rev. Microbiol.*, **7**, 415. *(6, 102)*
587 —, —, and LIND, C. J. (1942). *Proc. Nat. Acad. Sci., U.S.A.*, **28**, 243. *(54)*
588 —, and BURTON, J. C. (1938). *J. Agric. Sci.*, **28**, 307. *(44)*
589 —, LEE, S. B., and WYSS, O. (1941). *J. Biol. Chem.*, **139**, 81. *(54, 112)*
590 —, and UMBREIT, W. W. (1937). *Zentr. Bakteriol. Parasitenk*, Abt. II, **96**, 402, *(44)*
591 —, UMBREIT, W. W. and LEE, S. B. (1938). *Biochem. J.*, **32**, 2084. *(54)*
592 —, and WAGNER, F. C. (1935). *Trans. Wisc. Acad. Sci.*, **30**, 43. *(42)*
593 WILSON, T. G. G. and ROBERTS, E. R. (1954). *Biochim. Biophys. Acta*, **15**, 568. *(98)*
594 WINFIELD, M. E. (1955). *Rev. Pure Appl. Chem. Roy. Soc. Aust.*, **5**, 217. *(114)*
595 WINTER, G. (1935). *Beitr. Biol. Pflanz.*, **23**, 295. *(62, 68, 70)*
596 WINTER, H. and BURRIS, R. H. (1964). *Plant Physiol.*, **39**, suppl. xx. *(101, 112)*
597 WINOGRADSKY, S. (1893). *Comp. rend. Acad. Sci., Paris*, **116**, 1385. *(2, 71)*
598 WIPF., L. (1939). *Botan. Gaz.*, **101**, 51. *(16)*
599 —, and COOPER, D. C. (1939). *Proc. Nat. Acad. Sci., U.S.A.*, **24**, 87. *(16)*
600 —, — (1940). *Amer. J. Bot.*, **27**, 821. *(16)*
601 WOLFE, M. (1954). *Ann. Bot., Lond.*, N.S. **18**, 299. *(89)*
602 WOLK, P. (1965). *Nature, Lond.*, **205**, 201. *(64)*
603 WOODS, D. D. and LASCELLES, J. (1954). *Symp. Soc. gen. Microbiol.*, **4**, 1. *(75)*
604 WORONIN, M. (1886). *Mem. Acad. Imp. Sci. St. Petersb.*, 7, Ser. **10**, (6) 1. *(33)*
605 WYSS, O. and WILSON, P. W. (1941). *Proc. Nat. Acad. Sci., U.S.A.*, **27**, 162. *(112)*
606 WYSS, O., LIND, C. J., WILSON, J. B. and WILSON, P. W. (1941). *Biochem. J.*, **35**, 845. *(112)*
607 YANKOVITCH, L. (1940). *Amer. Serv. Bot. Agron. Tunisie*, No. **303**. *(125)*
608 YU-FENG SHEN (1960). *Taiwania*, **7**, 1. *(68)*
609 ZIEGLER, H. and HÜSER, R. (1963). *Nature, Lond.*, **199**, 508. *(28)*
610 ZELITCH, I. (1951). *Proc. Nat. Acad. Sci., U.S.A.*, **37**, 559. *(94)*
611 —, ROSENBLUM, E. D., BURRIS, R. H. and WILSON, P. W. (1951). *J. Biol. Chem.*, **191**, 295. *(66, 80, 104, 110)*
612 ZIMMERMANN, A. (1902). *Jahrb. f. Wiss. Bot.*, **37**, 1. *(81)*

Index

blue-green algae (*cont.*)

fixing site in, 65, 108; nitrogen-fixing species, list of, 61; in paddy fields, 58, 128–9, 131; photo-reduction of nitrogen in, 107–8; photosynthetic lamellae, 59, 64–5, Plate 7*a*; pigments, 59, 65; as primary colonisers, 130, 132–3; purification of, 59, 60; in soil, 128–31, 134, 137; structure, 58–9

bog myrtle, *see Myrica gale*

bryophytes, associations with nitrogen-fixing algae, 3, 67–8

Caesalpinioideae, 4, 11

calcium, 53, 121

Calothrix, 3, 62–3, 94, 131; endophytic, 70; in marine habitats, 70, 133–4; nitrogen-fixing species of, 62; as primary colonisers, 132–3

Calothrix brevissima, 62, 131; *C. crustacea*, 62; *C. elenkinii*, 62; *C. parietina*, 62, 79, 134; *C. scopulorum*, 62

Candida utilis, 110

carbamyl phosphate, 111–12

carbohydrate : nitrogen ratio

in blue-green algae, 64–5; effect on heterocyst formation, 64; effect on extracellular nitrogen production, 65

in symbiotic plants, 39–44; effect on: extracellular nitrogen production, 43–4; fixation, 39–44; nodulation, 41–2

factors affecting, 39–42

carbon monoxide, effect on: free-living nitrogen-fixing organisms, 90, 93–4; cell-free extracts, 94; haemoglobin, 57, 93, symbiotic plants, 56–7

carbon skeletons in nitrogen fixation, 43, 86, 109–12; α-ketoglutarate, 109–10; ornithine cycle, 109, 110; production by host plant, 20; pyruvate, 109, 111, 116.

Casuarina, 2, 26–7, 35–6; distribution of, 27; nitrogen fixation by, 27, 35; nodules of, 30, 35, 126; nodule roots of, 30, 35; in soil fertility, 126–8

Casuarina equisetifolia, 2, 128

Casuarinales, 4

Cavicularia, association of *Nostoc* with, 68

Ceanothus, distribution of, 27; nitrogen-fixation by, 27; position of endophyte in, 31

cell autolysis, in preparing nitrogen-fixing cell-free extracts, 78

cell-free extracts, nitrogen-fixing, 5, 6, 9, 10, 65, 73, 77–80, 90, 93–4, 105–10, 112–16; additives required, list of, 79; light, effect on, 75, 86; ^{13}N, in studies on, 9; pH, effect on, 85; preparation of, 78

Ceratozamia, root nodules of, 37, 67–8, 70

Cercocarpus betuloides, root nodules of, 37

cereals, reported fixation by, 2

Chlorobacteriaceae, 72; characteristics of, 74–5

Chlorobium, 72; characteristics of, 74

Chlorogloea fritschii, 61–3, 79, 86

Chlorophyceae, as lichen phycobionts, 68

Chomelia, leaf nodules, 81–2

Chomelia asiatica, 82

Chromatium, 3, 72, 86, 90, 93, 106–7, 111; cell-free extracts of, 79, 106; characteristics of, 75

Chroococcales, 61

citrulline, in *Alnus*, 47; in non-nodulated angiosperms, 47; in *Nostoc*, 112

Cladonia impexa, 67

Clostridium, 3, 55–72, 78–80, 89, 91, 93–4, 104–10, 112–16, 136; carbamyl phosphate in, 112; cell-free extract studies on, 78–9, 93,

possible intermediate in nitrogen fixation, 99–102, 104–5

hydrogen acceptors, effect on nitrogen fixation, 114

hydrogen, molecular, 22, 112–16; evolution of, by free-living nitrogen-fixing organisms, 92, 107, 114, by *Podocarpus*, 36, by root nodules of legumes, 55; inhibits nitrogen fixation, by free-living organisms, 77, 92–3, 112, 115, by symbiotic forms, 54–5; possible mechanism of inhibition by, 115; as reducing source for nitrogen fixation, 79, 93, 105–7, 115–16

hydrogenase, 22; of bacteria, 71, 76–7, 79, 89–93, 99, 112, 116; of blue-green algae, 65, 93; carbon monoxide inhibits, 94; of *Clostridium*, requirement for fixation by *Azotobacter* nitrogenase, 79, 113; cobalt required for, 89; possible function of, 112–16; molybdenum in, 112–13; nature of, 89, 90, 113–14; inhibition, by air, 93, by carbon monoxide, 94, by molecular nitrogen, 92, 112; inter-relations with nitrogenase, 112–16; iron in, 90–1, 113; in root nodules, 36, 55; separation from nitrogenase, 113–14

hydroxylamine, possible intermediate in nitrogen fixation, 98–9, 100–5

hydroxylamine reductases, 101

hyponitrous acid, as possible intermediate in nitrogen fixation, 98–99

B-indolylacetic acid, effect of light on, 49; possible effect on nodulation, 14; in non-legume nodule rootlets, 30; production of, by rhizobia, 14, 43

infection threads, of legumes, 14–18, Plate 2a; of non-legumes, 29

inorganic ions in nitrogen fixation, in free-living organisms, 88–91, 94–5; in symbiotic plants, 39–43, 49–53

inorganic nitrogen fertiliser, contribution to soil fertility, 117

insects, association of *Azotobacter* with, 80

intermediates in nitrogen fixation, suspected, 97–105

iron, 36; in ferredoxin, 53, 90–1; requirement by free-living nitrogen-fixing plants, 53, 88, 90–1, 93, by symbiotic plants, 21–2, 50, 52–3

α-ketobutyric acid, in cell-free extract studies, 79, 105

α-ketoglutaric acid, 102, 104–5, 109–12; as carbon skeleton for fixed nitrogen, 109–10; in cell-free extract studies, 79, 105; formation of PCA from, 100, 104

key intermediate in nitrogen fixation, ammonia, as possible, 66, 80, 102–5; definition of, 102; hydrazine, as possible, 102, 104–105; hydroxylamine, as possible, 102–5

Kjeldahl analyses, in measurement of nitrogen fixation, 7

Klebsiella, in leaf nodules, 81–2; nitrogen fixation by, 72, 81–2

Krakatau, colonisation of, by blue-green algae, 132

lakes, nitrogen fixation in, 134–6

Laminaria, 98

leaf glands, 81

leaf nodules, 3, 81–2

legumes, 3, 4, 11–25, 41–57, 100, 102; use in agriculture, 11, 119–25; use of, by arable farmer, 122; artificial inoculation of, 119; in crop rotation, 123–4; distribution of nitrogen in, 124; excretory products of roots, 43–4,